Dragonflies
of the Southwest

A Beginner's
Pocket Guide

by Kathy Biggs

Azalea Creek

Publishing

Azalea Creek Publishing
308 Bloomfield Road
Sebastopol, CA 95472

Publishers Cataloging In Publication
Biggs, Kathy, 1945 -

> Common Dragonflies of the Southwest
> A Beginner's Pocket Guide / Kathy Biggs.

> Includes bibliographical references and index
> Library of Congress Card Number: 2003090595
> ISBN 0-9677934-1-6
> 1. Dragonflies - Identification 2. Damselflies -
> Identification. 3. South West, USA.
>   I.Title.
> QL520.2.U6   DC21 595.7.33

This book is dedicated to:

Those wonderful
members of the
DSA
(Dragonfly Society of the Americas)
who provided encouragement
and added so much
to my knowledge
of dragonflies

and
also to
my mother,
Lela Claypole,
who fostered
my love of nature

Table of Contents

Preface

The arid regions of the Southwest have a unique dragonfly fauna that has not been addressed by any other dragonfly guide, until now. Like birds and butterflies, dragonflies are beautiful, colorful, interesting and diverse creatures. Those adapted to life in the Southwest are frequently special and often uncommon in other areas of North America. With the expanding popularity of "dragon watching" and the availability of close-focus binoculars, there are now many people who are interested in watching, documenting and photographing the Southwest's interesting species.

This book's purpose is to help people identify the dragonflies that they see on outings and at their homes. Until recently, the only methods available for identifying dragonflies were studying wing venation patterns and examining terminal appendages of captured dragonflies in hand through a microscope. These techniques can be overwhelming to beginners, to say the least. Luckily many species can be identified using size, color, pattern, behaviors, habitat, time of year and your specific location.

Using a simple format, this book focuses on providing the necessary information for you to begin making dragonfly identifications. Descriptions of their life cycle are therefore only lightly touched upon. More information about these dragonflies, and also those that are uncommon within the SW, is available at this book's companion website. The website has information on all SW species with links to frequently updated distribution maps by county: **http://southwestdragonflies.net/**

The digital images of live scanned dragonflies that are used on the family heading pages preserve the dragonfly's dazzling true life colors. Dead dragonflies quickly loose their colors and start fading the moment they die. Because of this, dragonflies will never be collected for wall art.

How to Use This Book

After becoming familiar with this book and the species, take it into the field with you. It is organized by presenting the most common of the dragonflies and, then, the damselflies; grouping them within families by similarities in appearance:

<u>**DRAGONFLIES (ANISOPTERA)**</u>: Heavy bodied, large, strong fliers. They hold their wings out to their sides when at rest.

  Skimmers (Libellulidae): Common, showy, variably-sized. Perch horizontally on vegetation near still or slow waters.

  Emeralds (Corduliidae): Often dark, having brilliant metallic tones with emerald green eyes. Found in the mountains.

  Darners (Aeshnidae): Large, powerful fliers. Within genera Mosaic and Green Darners are quite similar in appearance. Most are colored with blue or green. Perch hanging vertically.

  Clubtails (Gomphidae): Fairly large. Males may have a club shape to the end of their abdomen. Usually brown & yellow or green. Found on moving water. They perch on ground or rocks.

  Mixed families: Three different families, all large-sized with black and yellow markings - Petaltail, Cruisers, & Spiketails.

<u>**DAMSELFLIES (ZYGOPTERA)**</u>: Common, small and slender. Weak flyers holding wings over or alongside back when at rest.

  Pond Damsels (Coenagrionidae): A large common family including Bluets (*Enallagma*), Dancers (*Argia*), Forktails (*Ischnura*) and others. Most are small with blue and black coloring although a few are red; most prefer still or slow waters.

  Spreadwings (Lestidae): Long and thin. They hold their wings mostly open when at rest. The family consists of Pond Spreadwings, which are long but thin and found along still waters, and Stream Spreadwings, which are longer and found where moving water occurs, even when the water is temporarily dried up.

  Broad-winged Damsels (Calopterygidae): Large and showy damselflies with color in their broad wings. Found along streams and rivers. This family includes the Jewelwings (*Calopteryx*) and Rubyspots (*Hetaerina*).

- -

NAME: The common name is listed above the scientific name. Scientific names are included as the dragonflies were not given common names until late 1996. Therefore, scientific names may be necessary when cross-referencing between this book and other sources. Also, please note that many current insect guides were printed before the standardized common names were established in 1996. You may still find non-standardized common names used in older sources.

PHOTO: A photograph of a male is at the top of each page. A small photo of the female, a different view or detail (as noted) is at the bottom of most pages. Because dragonfly coloring changes with maturity and even the temperature, patterning is much more useful than coloration when making identifications.

SIZE: The average length for each species is shown by a bold line in one of the dominant colors of the dragonfly. The minimum and maximum possible variations in length and wing span are below this line as a measurement in millimeters (25.4 mm per inch). Rulers are inside the covers.

DESCRIPTION: The most distinguishing features of the male dragonfly are given; then the differences in the female are noted. Immature males can be colored like females.

HABITAT: The dragonfly's breeding environment is described. Each species will most frequently be seen there. Dragonflies can and do range from this habitat while feeding.

FLIGHT PERIOD: The range of months in which adult dragonflies can be seen flying. This varies by elevation & latitude.

DISTRIBUTION: The state in the Southwest where the dragonfly can be found. Please see the maps by county at the book's companion website, **http://southwestdragonflies.net/**. The maps at the website are frequently updated because dragonfly distribution is still being determined. You can help dragonfly distribution researchers by keeping track of your sightings!

Viewing Dragonflies

Equipment: All you really need are your eyes, but optional items include shoes that can get wet (water shoes work wonderfully) or boots, binoculars (close-focus) &/or camera with zoom lens, "butterfly" net, a 10X or higher magnifying hand lens, glassine envelopes such as used by stamp collectors or zip-lock plastic baggies, and plenty of sunscreen. There is much still to be learned about dragonfly behavior, distribution, migration, etc. Take along a notepad to keep track of your observations by locality and date.

Timing: Dragonflies are best viewed on a calm, sunny day. When it is windy or cool they tend to hide away and await improved weather. The best opportunities to view them will usually be near a waterway, although they can fly miles away from the waters from which they emerged when searching for food; indeed, some even migrate!

Method: Dragonflies are best approached slowly. Line yourself up directly with the insect and then walk straight towards it. They are more likely to fly away if you walk crosswise while near them. Sometimes you can get so close to a dragonfly that regular binoculars can't focus. That is when close-focus binoculars or a camera with a zoom lens comes in handy.

Sometimes it is necessary to catch the dragonfly in order to identify it, using an insect net. Dragonfly wings, unlike the butterfly's, are not fragile; gentle handling will not harm them. Hold dragonflies by pinching their wings together, folded over their back. The hand lens is useful for looking at small body parts and segments. Dragonflies can also be cooled in an ice chest, thereby slowing their metabolism so that they will perch quietly for photographing and then they can be released, unharmed. Often photographing the dragonfly and then comparing the photo to pictures in the book is helpful in learning to recognize the species. After learning the dragonfly in hand, on the wing becomes easier.

Life of the Dragonfly

Eggs: Dragonflies start life as a tiny egg, not much larger than the period at the end of this sentence. Most scatter their eggs freely over a waterway or insert them into vegetation that is floating in or overhanging water. Some eggs hatch within weeks; others overwinter before hatching.

Nymphs/larvae: The larval stage is called a nymph or, more properly, a larva. Dragonfly larvae look like fierce dragons and crawl about underwater hunting for food. A unique feature is their *labium*, a lower lip that they project to hook prey. While damselfly larvae have feather-like gills at the end of their abdomen, dragonfly larvae do not. All go through about a dozen molts, or instars, before crawling out onto a stem or rock to emerge.

Emergence: After a period of time, from a month or two to even a few years of growing and molting, the larva crawls out of the water. Its skin then cracks over the thorax. The adult dragonfly slowly emerges from this old shell; some at first hang down from it limply. Then after its legs harden, it pulls itself upright and its body and wings begin to expand and harden. After an hour or more the new adult dragonfly flies off. The empty shell that is left behind is called the exuvia.

Adults: Adult dragonflies live for only several weeks. During this time they feed on mosquitoes, gnats and other small insects (at a rate of many a day), mature sexually, and mate.

Reproduction: Males defend territories awaiting the females or actively search for them. The male grasps the female with clasp-like holders at the end of his abdomen. Mating occurs in the "wheel" position. Females use ovipositors to insert their eggs into plant stems or scatter them over the water, sometimes ovipositing while in tandem flight with the male. The larvae that hatch develop without need of parenting.

Dragonflies
Anisoptera

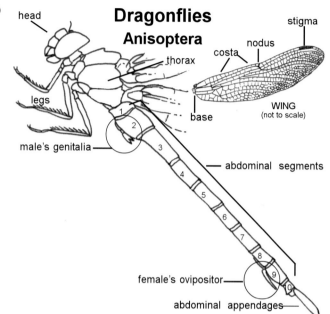

head

thorax

stigma

nodus

costa

WING
(not to scale)

legs

base

1

2

male's genitalia

3

abdominal segments

4

5

6

7

8

female's ovipositor

9

10

abdominal appendages

Large, heavy-bodied; ordinarily larger than damselflies.
Wings are held open & flat or down & forward when perched.
Large eyes are spaced very close together and in most families actually touch, creating a seam down the center.
Strong fliers; a few are even migratory.
Males have three terminal abdominal appendages and a bump (genitalia) under their second abdominal segment.
All females have only two terminal abdominal appendages and in many families they also have an ovipositor.
Most dragonflies lay their eggs directly into the water.
The southwest has at least 117 species representing all seven American dragonfly families.

Skimmers, Libellulidae

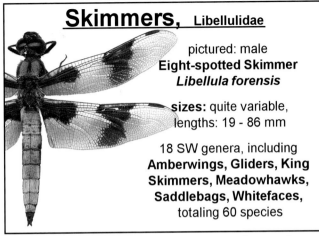

pictured: male
Eight-spotted Skimmer
Libellula forensis

sizes: quite variable,
lengths: 19 - 86 mm

18 SW genera, including
**Amberwings, Gliders, King
Skimmers, Meadowhawks,
Saddlebags, Whitefaces,**
totaling 60 species

males: showy nonmetallic colors; some wings patterned; bodies shorter than wingspans; eyes broadly touching

females: frequently more brown or paler than males but usually having similar wing markings; most splash oviposit

habitats: lakes and ponds; still waters of river pools

behaviors: most perch horizontally and fly out to hawk prey; males usually hover-guard ovipositing females

Amberwings - tiny; wings amber colored; arid regions
Gliders - strong flyers; often seen after weather change flying high overhead; perch hanging; known to migrate
King Skimmers - common; showy; wings held out flat
Meadowhawks - small; reddish; wings held downward
Saddlebags - dark areas at hind wing base; strong fliers
Whitefaces - small; dark body & eyes; bright white faces

Flame Skimmer *Sept. 24, 2005*
Libellula saturata Arivaca Cienega

William Zittrich

size: large, length 49 - 61 mm, wingspan 85 - 95 mm

male: unstriped thorax, abdomen, eyes, face, legs, stigma and appendages all red-orange; wings reddish out to slightly beyond nodus with a red streak along leading edge, red veins; hawks insects from perch

female: orange streak along leading edge of wings

habitat: ponds, lakes, slow streams, pools of rivers

S.P.

flight period: Feb. - Dec.

distribution: all Southwest

Neon Skimmer
Libellula croceipennis

Omar Bocanegra

size: large, length 54 - 59 mm, wingspan 74 - 90 mm

male: very wide bright neon red/pink abdomen; thorax and underside can be tawny; red on wings only adjacent to body and near leading edge, red does not extend to the nodus; stigma - dark outline; often perch in shade

female: tan/orange with noticeable pale stripe top of thorax; wings mostly clear

habitat: marshy creeks/ditches

flight period: April - October

distribution: CA, AZ, NM

C.W.

Red Rock Skimmer
Paltothemis lineatipes

Bob Parks

size: med/lg, length 44 - 54 mm, wingspan 90 - 95 mm

male: abd. intricately patterned with rusty red & black; face and eyes rusty red; rusty red on inner wings usually nearly to nodus, dark stigma; thorax can be olive-brown on sides; lands on rocks midstream

female: tan/brown; intricate pattern; no color in wings; no red on body

habitat: rocky streams

flight period: March - November

distribution: CA, UT, AZ, NM

R.M.

Western Meadowhawk
Sympetrum occidentale

Robert Behrstock

size: med, length 28 - 37 mm, wingspan 46 - 57 mm

male: deep red upper abdomen with black markings lower sides; black top segments 8 & 9; inner wings rusty out to nodus; thorax sides - 3 irregular black stripes; eyes & face dark rusty red; imm. male yellow like female

female: yellow where male is red; may have much less color in wings

habitat: weedy ponds, lakes

flight period: April - October

distribution: all Southwest

RAB

Cardinal Meadowhawk
Sympetrum illotum

David Bozsik

size: med, length 32 - 40 mm, wingspan 55 - 60 mm

male: cardinal red head, thorax, abdomen, wing veins; red on wings is diffuse and only close to body and near the leading edge; wings have very small dark streaks at extreme base; thorax sides have two small white spots; body with no black, appears stubby; red legs

female: less colorful; pale red legs

habitat: ponds, lakes

flight period: January - November

distribution: CA, NV, AZ, NM

S.A.

Red-veined Meadowhawk
Sympetrum madidum

Ray Bruun

size: med, length 40 - 45 mm, wingspan 58 - 62 mm

male: dark red face & abd.; thoracic stripes partly obscured by red; underside abd. dark, dark spots seg. 8 & 9; distinct red wing "stripe" touches black or dark red fairly long stigma; no black areas near wing base; jet black legs

female: tawny body; seg. 1 & 2 bulbous; dull yellow face; wings like male; black legs

habitat: ponds, marshes, lakes

flight period: April - September

distribution: CA, NV, UT?, CO

RAB

Yellow-legged Meadowhawk
Sympetrum vicinum

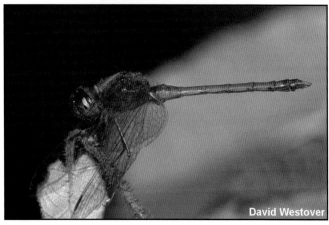

David Westover

size: sm/med, **length 26 - 35 mm,** wingspan 42 - 46 mm

male: all red when mature; immature yellow; no stripes on thorax; top & sides of abdomen with greatly reduced or no black; slender, thin yellow-brown legs; wings clear with yellow-amber at base; often last species in the fall

female: like immature male but with very prominent, distinctive, triangular ovipositor on "tail"

habitat: lakes, ponds, slow streams

flight period: June - November

distribution: mts. of CA, CO, AZ, NM

K.B.

Red-tailed Pennant
Brachymesia furcata

Robert Behrstock

size: med, length 38 - 46 mm, wingspan 66 - 73 mm

male: Meadowhawk-like; stocky; face & abdomen red; thorax brown; each abd. seg. with thin dark ring, black spots atop seg. 8 & 9; wings have dark veins, amber at base with long stigma; jet black legs; "ski-tipped" append.

female: brown with pale stripe between wings & at abd. base; sm. black spots last segs.

habitat: ponds, lakes, canals

flight period: May - Nov.

distribution: so. CA, AZ

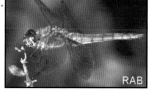

RAB

Cherry-faced Meadowhawk
Sympetrum internum

George Doerksen

size: small/med, length 29 - 36 mm, wingspan 46 - 52 mm

male: overall dark red; plain brown-red thorax; dull cherry red face (imm. - tawny yellow) with dark line; black legs; clear wings with reddish veins, basal amber wash; triangular black marks low on abdomen sides

female: less colorful; wings at base extensively amber colored

habitat: wet meadows; slow waters

flight period: June - October

distribution: CA, NV, UT, CO, NM

N.D.

White-faced Meadowhawk
Sympetrum obtrusum

Greg Lasley

size: med, length 30 - 39 mm, wingspan 52 - 56 mm

male: white face; abdomen & thorax red; thoracic side stripes on immatures only, no top stripes; distinct black triangles lower sides of abdomen; wing veins not reddish

female: similar or golden; face greenish white

habitat: marshes, lakes, wet meadows in highlands

flight period: May - October; more common in the fall

distribution: all SW mts. but AZ

G.L.

Striped Meadowhawk
Sympetrum pallipes

Ray Bruun

---

size: med, length 34 - 38 mm, wingspan 52 - 58 mm

male: mature red, immature golden; 2 pale top & side thoracic stripes (top stripes lacking in ALL other meadowhawks); pale face; clear wings, one rust vein; velvet-like dots where wings join body; rounded black marks low abd.

female: tawny or red brown

habitat: ponds and lakes

flight period: April - Nov. more common in fall

distribution: all SW

R.B.

Saffron-winged Meadowhawk
Sympetrum costiferum

Robert Behrstock

size: med, length 31 - 39 mm, wingspan 50 - 56 mm

male: body red when mature; immature golden; leading wing edges and veins golden; stigma yellow with black edges; underside of abdomen black; legs striped black

female: like immature male

habitat: woody marshes, ponds, lakes, creeks

flight period: June - Nov.

distribution: CA, NV, UT, CO, NM (not yet found AZ)

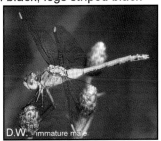

D.W. - immature male

Variegated Meadowhawk
Sympetrum corruptum

Steve Potter

size: med, length 33 - 43 mm, wingspan 60 - 64 mm

male: quite variable; olive-green/gray and reddish plaid, turns redder as it ages, unique white "porthole-like" spots low on abdomen; thoracic stripes not always complete but end in yellow spot; cranberry eyes; stigma bicolored

female: less red; more muted

habitat: all slow water

flight period: year round, migratory; may overwinter

distribution: all Southwest

R.B.

Roseate Skimmer
Orthemis ferruginea

Dustin Huntington

size: med/lg, length **46 - 55 mm,** wingspan 79 - 92 mm

male: thorax rose pink and/or plum pruinescence; rose pruinescence on abd.; wings clear, very narrowly tipped with brown; top of head metallic black when mature

female: orange-brown; complex pale pattern thorax sides, lt. stripe top center; noticeable flanges lower abd.

habitat: ponds, lakes, canals

flight period: all year in its most southern regions

distribution: all SW states

B.P.

Mexican Amberwing
Perithemis intensa

Sept 3% 2005
Arivaca Cienega

Peter Moulton

size: small, length 23 - 29 mm, wingspan 41- 44 mm

male: small & stubby; all orange, even the wings which have pale orange stigma; thorax can be tawny; very unwary; tend to perch on twigs; immatures more yellow

female: orange body; wings - amber-orange bands with dark spots, darker stigma than male

habitat: ponds, lakes, slow streams, pools of rivers

R.M.

flight period: March - November

distribution: CA, NV, AZ, NM

Eastern Amberwing
Perithemis tenera

Sept. 24, 2005
Arivaca Cienega

Greg Lasley

size: very small, length 19 - 25 mm, wingspan 33 - 43

male: tiny but stubby; wings yellowish-orange, may have small dark spots, red stigma; thorax brownish with two pale side stripes; patterned abdomen; mimics wasp behavior by waving wings and abdomen up and down

female: brown body; variable dark patched/spotted wings

habitat: ponds, lakes, slow streams, even brackish waters

flight period: May - October

distribution: CO, AZ, NM

D.M.

Red Saddlebags
Tramea onusta

Dave Biggs

size: med, **length 41 - 49 mm,** wingspan 80 - 90 mm

male: mostly red or rusty red including eyes; thorax tawny; black spots top of segments 8-10; hind wings have broad red saddle mark; powerful flier; frequently perch with abdomen lowered; migratory. *Striped Saddlebags* - male & female have 2 broad side stripes on thorax

female: tawny; black spots abd.

habitat: warm shallow ponds

flight period: Feb. - November

distribution: all SW; *AZ (stray)

M.H.

Black Saddlebags
Tramea lacerata

David Westover

size: large, **length 47 - 55 mm,** wingspan 95 - 102 mm

male: black body; diffuse yellow spot top of abdomen; broad black saddle mark on hind wings; folded long legs give thorax bulky look in flight; powerful flier; usually perch horizontally; migratory

female: similar, more yellow spots

habitat: ponds, lakes, creeks, and slow areas of rivers

flight period: March - November

distribution: all Southwest

R.M.

Marl Pennant
Macrodiplax balteata

Rosser Garrison

size: med, **length 35 - 44 mm,** wingspan 57 - 74 mm

male: wide head; dark eyes; small dark basal patches on wings; dark body and abdomen with thin pale rings

female: wings like male; thorax & abdomen yellow on golden brown; abd. tip dark; thorax sides - 3 pale areas

habitat: brackish coastal ponds, desert oases; specializes on saline & especially alkaline habitats

D.H.

flight period: May - September

distribution: CA, AZ, NM

Checkered Setwing
Dythemis fugax

Bob Parks

size: med, **length 42 - 51 mm,** wingspan 72 - 78 mm

male: dark with pale spots top of abdomen; lacy brown basal wing patches; bright red face and eyes. **Black** and **Swift Setwing** - face dark; no basal wing patches; Swift's tips brown. **Mayan Setwing** (AZ only) - male is red; female is orange-brown with dark wingtips; rare.

female: like male; wing tips brown

habitat: marshes, ponds, slow waters

flight period: April - December

distribution: AZ, NM

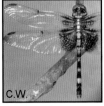

C.W.

Desert Whitetail
Libellula subornata

Dave Biggs

size: med, **length 40 - 52 mm,** wingspan 64 - 76 mm

male: pruinose white abdomen; wings - 2 narrow zigzag black bands, middle third usually fills in dark; basal half of wings - extensive white pruinosity; dark appendages

female: brown body; 2 pale, jagged thoracic stripes; row of yellow side dashes on abdomen; each wing has dual zigzag bands, clear wing tips

habitat: desert springs, ponds, lakes

flight period: April - November

distribution: all SW deserts

D.B.

Common Whitetail
Libellula lydia

Greg Lasley

size: med, **length 39 - 48 mm,** wingspan 65 - 75 mm

male: broad abdomen matures gleaming white; wings - broad dark band 1/3 width, small black basal bar, small white area only at wing base; top of append. frosty; imm. - body marked like female; wings like mature male, lack white

female: 3 dark wing spots; wide brown body; yellow side dashes angled, separated

habitat: marshes, streams

flight period: February - Nov.

distribution: all Southwest

Twelve-spotted Skimmer
Libellula pulchella

Alan Wight

size: large, length 51 - 58 mm, wingspan 84 - 92 mm

male: 3 dark spots each wing, including wing tip, 3 white spots develop between them as the body ages; abdomen develops a bluish-white pruinosity as it matures

female: brown abd. - continuous yellow side stripe; wings - 3 dark spots, no white spots; compare to female **Co. Whitetail**

D.M.

habitat: ponds, lakes, rivers

flight period: April - October

distribution: all Southwest

Eight-spotted Skimmer
Libellula forensis

Rod Miller

size: med/lg, length 49 - 51 mm, wingspan 77 - 80 mm

male: 2 dark spots each wing, outer one shaped like a numeral "8" and extends from leading to trailing edge, 3 white spots, tips clear; pruinose blue abd. & thorax top

female: brown body; yellow side stripe dashed but forms straight line; wings like male's, may develop white spots

habitat: ponds, lakes, ditches

flight period: April - October

distribution: all; rare AZ

D.Ho.

Widow Skimmer
Libellula luctuosa

Steven Bruun

size: med, length 38 - 50 mm, wingspan 76 - 80 mm

male: body becomes pruinose pale blue; inside half of wings blackish-brown, outer wing sides develop extensive white pruinescence; expanding its range within the SW

female: brown with yellow side stripes; dark wing tips

habitat: ponds, lakes, pools of rivers & creeks, marshes

flight period: April - Nov.

distribution: all Southwest

G.L.

Hoary Skimmer
Libellula nodisticta

Rod Miller

size: med/lg, length 46 - 52 mm, wingspan 76 - 82 mm

male: thorax and abdomen pruinose blue-gray; thorax of immature has 2 broken yellow stripes; wings have small dark area at base & nodus, basal dark wing area becomes surrounded by white, black stigma; no other white on wings

female: dark gray/brown with row of yellow dashes along abdomen side

habitat: springs; spring-fed streams

flight period: April - September

distribution: all SW; sporadic, sparse

R.B.

Bleached Skimmer
Libellula composita

Robert Behrstock

size: med, length 42 - 49 mm, wingspan 70 - 88 mm

male: pruinose blue body becomes bleached/washed out in appearance; pale eyes; white face; wings - dark spot at base & usually also at nodus, dark veins; pale costa (vein along leading edge of the wing); dark stigma

female: wings like male; abdomen - interrupted pale yellow stripes, pale eyes & face

habitat: alkaline ponds; springs

flight period: May - September

distribution: CA, NV, UT, AZ, NM

D.H.

Comanche Skimmer
Libellula comanche

Dustin Huntington

size: med/lg, length 45 - 57 mm, wingspan 70 - 88 mm

male: pruinose blue with pearly blue or greenish eyes; white face; wings clear, white stigma with dark on outside edge, but position variable; immature - thorax striped

female: brown and pale yellow with dark stripe along abdomen back; face & stigma pale; wings often have darkish area tips &/or leading edge

habitat: ponds, ditches, canals

flight period: May - November

distribution: CA, NV, UT, AZ, NM

K.W.

Blue Dasher
Pachydiplax longipennis

William Zittrich

size: med, length 32 - 45 mm, wingspan 48 - 50 mm

male: pruinose blue, developing dark tip, tan under seg. 1-3; striped thorax can become all blue; teal green/blue eyes; distinctive white face with black between the eyes; wings, often held downward, can show brown tinted areas

female: rectangular buff marks on dark background; no other is like it; white face

habitat: ponds, slow waters

flight period: Feb. - Nov.

distribution: all Southwest

G.L.

Western Pondhawk
Erythemis collocata

Steve Potter

size: med, length 39 - 42 mm, wingspan 63 - 65 mm

male: pruinose blue with bright green face; deep blue eyes; dark appendages; immature like female, thorax last to turn blue, no dark patches/spots/bands; usually perches low, often on or near the ground or on floating vegetation

female: emerald green body - thin dark line along middle top; some yellow near tip

habitat: ponds, creek pools

flight period: Feb. - Nov.

distribution: all Southwest

R.B.

Eastern Pondhawk
Erythemis simplicicollis

Dave McShaffrey - young male

size: med, length 36 - 48 mm, wingspan 63 - 65 mm

male: pruinose blue with green face; dark blue eyes; emerges green like female, sides of thorax last area to become blue; displays white appendages held upward

female: emerald green body with pale and dark areas along abdomen; white append-ages; spout-like ovipositor

habitat: ponds, creek pools

flight period: yr. round in so.

distribution: CO, AZ, NM

D.M.

Great Pondhawk
Erythemis vesiculosa

Robert Behrstock

size: large, length 55 - 65 mm, wingspan 80 - 82 mm

male: narrow long green abd. with dark and pale bands; eyes green-gray; appendages white; juvenile has green stigma; wary; often flies with abdomen raised 30 degrees

female: like male; eyes dark brown; thin abdomen with short inconspicuous ovipositor

habitat: ponds; pools of creeks and rivers

flight period: April - Sept.

distribution: rare; CO, AZ, NM

c.w.

Spot-winged Glider
Pantala hymenaea

Steve Potter

size: med, length 43 - 51 mm, wingspan 86 - 96 mm

male: robust; body patterned golden browns, generally darker brown than **Wandering Glider**; tawny or rufous stigma; red face; clear front wing; wide hind wing - small round dark basal spot (often difficult to see in flight); strong gliding flight; migrate; often seen after weather change

female: like male, patterned less boldly; yellow face

habitat: ponds (even temporary), lakes, yards

flight period: March - October; all year in south

distribution: all Southwest

Wandering Glider
Pantala flavescens

Greg Lasley

size: med, length 44 - 51 mm, wingspan 83 - 91 mm

male:45 golden orange-yellow-brown body, dark pattern along abdomen top; yellowish face; mature has red eyes; broad clear wings possibly with yellow wash at tips and base but no dark basal spot; golden stigma; hind wing very wide - strong gliding flight; vagrant, migrant; follows weather fronts

female: similar; male & females feed in mixed swarms

habitat: open still waters; frequently found in yards

flight period: March - November, all year in south

distribution: all Southwest; a cosmopolitan species

Filigree Skimmer
Pseudoleon superbus

Dustin Huntington

size: med, **length 38 - 45 mm,** wingspan 63 - 73 mm

male: wings variably dark & lacy, sometimes almost all dark; brown body with pale chevrons ages to nearly all black; eyes are striped and when mature are nearly all black; perch low, often on rocks/debris, often in oblique posture

female: lace pattern on wings more open; spoutlike ovipositor

habitat: rocky, clear streams

flight period: March - Nov.

distribution: AZ, NM

G.W.

Four-spotted Skimmer
Libellula quadrimaculata

Alan Wight

size: med, length 40 - 46 mm, wingspan 66 - 72 mm

male: olive to orangish-brown body, thorax somewhat hairy; abdomen tapered with yellow dashes on sides, tip darker; leading wing edges usually orangish with small dark spots at nodus, larger dark area hind wing base

female: very similar

habitat: bogs, marshes, lakes, streams in mt. areas; acidic waters

flight period: April - October

distribution: all Southwest

D.D.

Black Meadowhawk
Sympetrum danae

Robert Behrstock

size: small, **length 26 - 32 mm,** wingspan 42 - 46 mm

male: mature - all black including face; immature shows complex yellow markings thorax sides including three yellow dots in a black belt, yellow areas along abdomen and on face; clear wings; legs all black; very petite

female: like immature male; variable amber wing wash

habitat: all slow mt. waters

flight period: May - Nov.

distribution: all (mt. areas only)

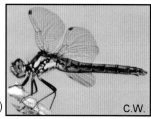

C.W.

Plateau Dragonlet
Erythrodiplax basifusca

Peter Moulton

size: sm/med, length 24 - 34 mm, wingspan 43 - 53 mm

male: black abdomen develops thin blue pruinosity on segments 1-7; face tawny to metallic black; wings clear except hind wing often with small basal dark amber patch. ***Black-winged** & ****Seaside Dragonlet** similar; Seaside at saline lakes, all black

female: yellow, brown side stripe

habitat: marshy ponds, lakes

flight period: March - Nov.

distribution: *AZ, **NM

RAB

Hudsonian Whiteface
Leucorrhinia hudsonica

David Westover

size: small, **length 26 - 30 mm,** wingspan 44 - 57 mm

male: dainty; dark eyes; bright white face; red thorax; abd. black with red spots along top of segments 1-7 (yellow in immature); costa yellow from nodus. ***Boreal Whiteface -** continuous broad red stripe along top of abdomen, which includes segment 8

female: same or black with yellow

habitat: sedge marshes

flight period: April - October

distribution: CA, NV, *UT, *CO

D.W.

Crimson-ringed / Red-waisted Whiteface
Leucorrhinia glacialis/L. proxima

George Doerksen - Crimson Ringed

size: medium, **length 32 - 38 mm,** wingspan 52 - 60 mm

male: black with only segs. 1 & 2 and thorax marked with red; bright white face; to identify to species use wing venation illustrations on SW website and appendage length:
L. glacialis - lower append. half length of uppers.
L. proxima lower's 2/3rds length.

female: same or yellow & black

habitat: boggy ponds, mt. lakes

flight period: May - October

Crimson Ringed - R.B.

distribution: see p.152

Dot-tailed Whiteface
Leucorrhinia intacta

George Doerksen

size: med, **length 29 - 35 mm,** wingspan 48 - 52 mm

male: black body & head with bright white face; mature male has large yellow dot only on seg. 7; immature marked like female, as it matures, there are transitional stages

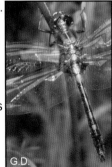

female: like male or showing yellow atop abdomen, including segment 7

habitat: spring-fed ponds, bogs, lakes

flight period: May - September

distribution: mts. of all SW but AZ

G.D.

Pale-faced Clubskimmer
Brechmorhoga mendax

Rod Miller

size: large, length 52 - 64 mm, wingspan 68 - 86 mm

male: gray; pale face, forehead & thoracic stripes; club-shaped narrow abdomen, seg. 7 has 2 very closely spaced pale spots top; patrols streams & rivers. **Masked Clubskimmer** occurs in southeast AZ; forehead black

female: like male but wings tips and small basal area brown; abdomen not as clubbed

habitat: rivers and streams

flight period: March - November

distribution: CA, NV, UT, AZ, NM

R.B. - side view

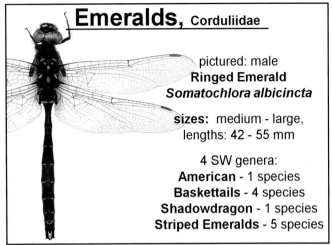

Emeralds, Corduliidae

pictured: male
Ringed Emerald
Somatochlora albicincta

sizes: medium - large,
lengths: 42 - 55 mm

4 SW genera:
American - 1 species
Baskettails - 4 species
Shadowdragon - 1 species
Striped Emeralds - 5 species

males: often dark having brilliant metallic tones, although some have bodies that are patterned; all with emerald green eyes; abdomens expanded at midpoint

females: like males; bodies stouter, even shaped

habitats: wooded ponds and streams in the mountains

behaviors: early mass emergences; perch by hanging; strong, fast, erratic fliers; sometimes hard to find, scarce

Baskettails - non-metallic colors; brown and yellow patterned; hairy thorax; found at lower elevations than others; often fly at waist height along trails and paths
American Emerald - metallic green; forked appendages
Striped Emeralds - metallic green; high fliers; appendages not forked; often thin pale rings around abdomen

Dot-winged Baskettail
Epitheca petechialis

Curtis Williams

size: med, length 41 - 43 mm, wingspan 62 - 64 mm

male: mature's eyes green, contrast with dull brown flattened spindle shaped abdomen, yellow side spots; thorax hairy; clear wings - tiny brown spots leading edge.
Beaverpond & **Spiny Baskettail** similar; lack spots on wings; both CA only; Spiny is rare in CA

female: like male, body broader

habitat: slow waters in forests

flight period: Feb. - Sept.

distribution: CO, NM

C.W.

American Emerald
Cordulia shurtleffii

Dennis Paulson

sizes: med, length 42 - 50 mm, wingspan 60 - 65 mm

male: emerald green eyes; dark hairy thorax with green metallic tones; abdomen enlarged mid-length with single thin white ring between segments 2 & 3; appendages splayed. ***Ringed Emerald (Somatochlora albicincta)** similar but has a white ring on each segment

female: like male; body cylindrical

habitat: wooded ponds, bogs

flight period: May - September

distribution: *CA, NV, UT, CO (mts)

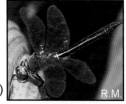

R.M.

Mountain Emerald
Somatochlora semicircularis

Rosser Garrison

size: med/lg, length 47 - 55 mm, wingspan 62 - 70 mm

male: emerald green eyes; dark hairy thorax, sides have two yellow markings within metallic green area; dark abd. enlarged at mid-length, may show yellow spots on sides of seg. 5-8; appendages point inwards, "pincher-like"

female: similar to male; broader abdomen; cerci 3 mm or more, female **American Emerald's** cerci 2 mm or less

habitat: ponds, sedge meadows with small streams

flight period: June - September

distribution: CA, NV, UT, CO, NM (in mountains)

Darners, Aeshnidae

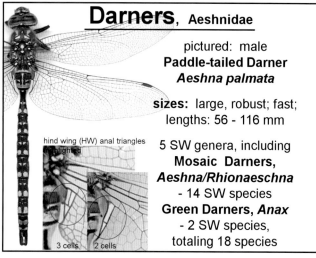

pictured: male
Paddle-tailed Darner
Aeshna palmata

sizes: large, robust; fast;
lengths: 56 - 116 mm

5 SW genera, including
Mosaic Darners,
Aeshna/Rhionaeschna
- 14 SW species
Green Darners, *Anax*
- 2 SW species,
totaling 18 species

hind wing (HW) anal triangles highlighted

3 cells   2 cells

males: brilliant blue and/or green with brown

females: 2 or more forms, one like males; others green
and/or yellow instead of blue; brown and/or purple base

habitats: lakes, creeks, rivers; fields

behaviors: usually seen in flight; patrol waterways but
also often seen catching insects over fields; perch by
hanging vertically; oviposit into floating vegetation; some
swarm; some migrate; when cool, blue coloration darkens

Mosaic Darners, *Aeshna/Rhionaeschna* - large bluish
eyes; mosaic pattern; quite similar; upper append. differ
Green Darners, *Anax* - large green eyes, both very
similar except for **Giant Darner**'s much larger size; the
Common Green Darner is known to be a mass migrant

Mosaic Darners, *Aeshna/Rhionaeschna*

To identify them, use color of the line across face, presence (*Rhionaeschna*) or lack (*Aeshna*) of a small bump under first segment, the presence or lack of paired blue spots on abd. underside, the presence and/or shape of thoracic top and side stripes, shape of upper appendages and the ovipositor length. Use of an identification key is often necessary.

---

female Blue-eyed Darner
Rhionaeschna multicolor
color form - non-male like

Darner exuvia

The exoskeleton left behind when a darner nymph metamorphoses to become a flier.

Bob Claypole

Chris Heaivilin

Blue-eyed Darner
Rhionaeschna multicolor

O.B.   Bob Miller

size: large, length 60 - 74 mm, wingspan 86 - 98 mm

male: bright blue eyes & face; broad blue stripes thorax sides and top; abdomen appears almost all blue when in flight, but is mosaic blue, black and copper; appendages forked - wrench shaped when seen from side; spots top seg. 10 pale and widely separated; bump under 1st seg.

female: facial line pale brown; bump under first segment

habitat: ponds, lakes, slow streams

flight period: February - November

distribution: all Southwest

Blue-eyed appendages

California Darner
Rhionaeschna californica

D.D.   Ron LeValley

size: large, length 56 - 64 mm, wingspan 70 - 82 mm

male: small for family; sky blue eyes & spots, immature grayer; face pale blue with black line; thin pale blue thoracic side stripes curve slightly backwards; thin stripes or none thorax top; append. simple, without small spine; spots on seg. 10 closer together than on 9; bump under 1st seg.

female: facial line black; bump under first segment

habitat: ponds, lakes, slow streams

flight period: February - August

distribution: CA, NV, CO, UT

California appendages

Sedge Darner
Aeshna juncea

Chris Heaivilin

size: very lg, length 66 - 75 mm, wingspan 82 - 98 mm

male: thorax side stripes relatively broad, straight edged but tapered, stripes are blue above, greenish-yellow and widest at bottom; face greenish blue with black line; large, closely spaced spots on segment 10; HW anal triangle - two cells; appendages paddle shaped, no spine

female: black facial line; no bump under 1st segment

habitat: slow waters in forested areas

flight period: June - October

distribution: UT, CO, NM

Sedge appendages   D.P.

Variable Darner
Aeshna interrupta

R.B.

Dave Biggs

size: very lg, length 62 - 77 mm, wingspan 89 - 102 mm

male: dark; thorax side stripes interrupted or very narrow; top stripes very narrow or missing; dark bluish eyes; face pale greenish yellow - black line; abd. spots sky-blue, sm. spots seg. 10 more widely separated than on 9, no spots underside; HW anal triangle - 2 cells; append. lack spine

female: facial line black; no bump under first segment

habitat: mt. lakes, ponds, bogs

flight period: May - October

distribution: all Southwest

Variable appendages

Walker's Darner
Aeshna walkeri

R.B.

Pete Haggard

size: very large, length 72 - 77 mm, wingspan 87 - 100 mm

male: face, thoracic stripes nearly white; clear wings, black veins & stigma; abd. spots large, fewer small spots than other *Aeshna*; no spots top seg. 10, those on seg. 9 fused; no blue spots underside; flared paddle-shaped append. with small spine; 3 cells hw anal triangle; flies late in season

female: facial line black; no bump; jet black stigma

habitat: mostly creeks & streams

flight period: May - November

distribution: CA, NV

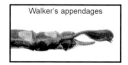

Walker's appendages

Shadow Darner
Aeshna umbrosa

R.B. - female Ray Bruun - male, in hand

size: very large, length 67 - 78 mm, wingspan 86 - 100 mm

male: sometimes appears darker, showing less blue than other Mosaic Darners or as blue as most; frontal thoracic stripe green; paired blue spots underside of abd.; no blue spots top of segment 10; appendages paddle-shaped with small spine; 3 cells in hw anal triangle; flies late in season

female: chocolate brown; no bump; pale spots underside

habitat: often flies in the shade

flight period: Feb. - November

distribution: CA, NV, UT, CO, NM

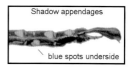

Shadow appendages

blue spots underside

Paddle-tailed Darner
Aeshna palmata

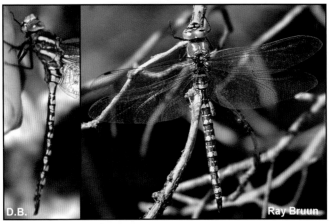

D.B.
Ray Bruun

size: very lg, length 62 - 75 mm, wingspan 84 - 97 mm

male: face & thoracic stripes greenish; black line across face; clear wings; in SW, blue spots on top of 9th & 10th abdominal segments usually fused (see p. 58); many small spots; underside of abd. dark; 3 cells in HW anal triangle; flared paddle-shaped appendages with small spine

female: facial line black; no bump under first segment

habitat: ponds, lakes, small streams

flight period: May - November

distribution: all SW forested areas

Paddle-tailed appendages

Persephone's Darner
Aeshna persephone

Ann Johnson

size: very lg, length 72 - 79 mm, wingspan 100 - 103 mm

male: thorax side stripes broad, parallel sided, yellow; blue eyes; pale green face, black facial line; sky blue mosaic pattern on abd. less pronounced than on other *Aeshna*; fused spot seg. 9 tri-lobed, spots on 10 reduced or missing; appendages paddle shaped with small spine

female: wide yellow side stripes; no bump under 1st seg.

habitat: desert canyons, along shaded streams

flight period: July - November

distribution: CO, AZ, NM; rare all

Persephone's appendages A.J.

Lance-tipped Darner
Aeshna constricta

Ann Johnson

size: very lg, length 65 - 73 mm, wingspan 88 - 100 mm

male: face pale green-yellow; fine brown facial line; side stripes on thorax indented; abdomen's spots blue-green inc. seg. 10. Similar **Canada D.** (CA only) - underside abd. has paired blue spots. *****Lake D.** - black facial line; append. toothed, no spine; HW anal triangle with only 2 cells

female: brown with blue-green/yellow spots; no bump

habitat: slow streams and ponds in open marshes

flight period: July - October

distribution: NV?, *UT, *CO, NM

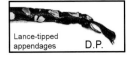

Lance-tipped appendages   D.P.

Riffle Darner
Oplonaeschna armata

photo rotated 90°

female ovipositing - **Doug Danforth** - male, in hand

size: very lg, length 66 - 75 mm, wingspan 92 - 110 mm

male: very similar to Mosaic darners; deep blue eyes; strongly indented side thoracic stripes blue above, yellow below; abd. spots a bit smaller than on Mosaic darners; append. paddle shaped with spine & a toothed projection near tip; top of segment 10 has a fingerlike projection

female: short; yellow, blue &/or green spots; no bump

habitat: rocky streams in oak & pine woodlands

flight period: May - November

distribution: CA & UT (rare), AZ, NM

Riffle appendages   D.D.

Common Green Darner
Anax junius

Bob Parks

size: very large, 63 - 84 mm, wingspan 92 - 103 mm

male: more solidly colored than Mosaic Darners; green eyes and yellow-green face; solid green thorax; blue abdomen with wide dark stripe on top; wings can be clear or show yellowish tinge; abdomen carried straight in flight

female: most purplish brown with green; rarer form colored like male

P.H.

habitat: fields and waterways

flight period: all months, migratory

distribution: all Southwest

Giant Darner
Anax walsinghami

Rod Miller

size: huge, male 99 - 116 mm, wingspan 115 - 137 mm

male: coloring like **Common Green Darner** but very long blue & dark patterned abd. which droops in flight; solid green thorax; eyes blue on top

female: like male; smaller; less blue; 88 - 98 mm, wingspan 112 -122 mm

habitat: canyon & spring-fed streams, marshes, lakes in arid areas

flight period: April - October

distribution: CA, NV, UT, AZ, NM

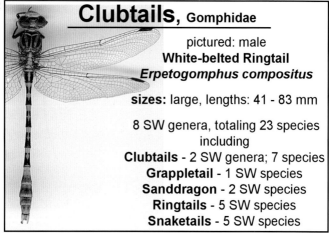

Clubtails, Gomphidae

pictured: male
White-belted Ringtail
Erpetogomphus compositus

sizes: large, lengths: 41 - 83 mm

8 SW genera, totaling 23 species
including
Clubtails - 2 SW genera; 7 species
Grappletail - 1 SW species
Sanddragon - 2 SW species
Ringtails - 5 SW species
Snaketails - 5 SW species

males: most have an enlarged area at end of abdomen; black, brown, green and/or yellow patterned; clear wings with wide stigmas; small eyes widely separated; sprawling legs; well camouflaged; no blue or red coloring

females: often yellow where male green; bodies cylindrical

habitats: life cycle of 2 years usually in rivers, streams

behaviors: males perch on ground/rocks at beach in sunlit areas; females more often found out on vegetation

Clubtails - narrow pale triangles down top of black/brown abdomen; some occur at ponds and lakes
Grappletail - abdomen thin & less patterned than others
Sanddragons - narrow clubbed abdomen; short legs
Ringtails - ringed appearance to abdomen; short legs
Snaketails - 5 very similar species; most in arid lands

Grappletail
Octogomphus specularis

Doug Danforth

size: large, length 49 - 53 mm, wingspan 60 - 82 mm

male: face yellow, eyes dark gray; thorax top - large bold gray-green/yellow urn shaped mark; very thin abdomen almost all black showing less yellow than any other SW clubtail; black legs & stigma; appendages grapple-like

female: thin yellow line top of cylindrical abdomen

habitat: rivers with riffles in wooded hillsides

flight period: April - October

distribution: CA, NV

R.M.

Gray Sanddragon
Progomphus borealis

Peter Moulton

size: large, length 56 - 62 mm, wingspan 66 - 72 mm

male: yellow face; thorax sides - large gray patches; dull pale yellow triangles top of very thin black abdomen; costa yellow; upper appendages yellow, lowers dark, same as **Common Sanddragon**; both arch abdomen when perching

female: more gray/green

habitat: sandy rivers, lakes

flight period: March - Oct.

distribution: CA, NV, UT, AZ, NM (not yet found in CO)

RAB

Common Sanddragon
Progomphus obscurus

Robert Behrstock

size: med/lg, length 47- 55 mm, wingspan 60 - 68 mm

male: very similar to **Gray Sanddragon**, but with two distinct yellow stripes side of thorax; yellow face; on both species the stripes top of thorax form a "W"; same pale yellow triangles top of very thin black abdomen; often lacks thin yellow rings at clubbed end on seg. 8 & 9; costa yellow

female: less clubbed; paler coloration

habitat: sandy ponds, streams

flight period: April - Sept.

distribution: CO, NM

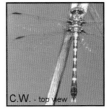

C.W. - top view

White-belted Ringtail
Erpetogomphus compositus

Dave Biggs

size: med/lg, length 46 - 55 mm, wingspan 60 - 70 mm

male: thorax intricately marked green, yellow, black, middle side stripe the "white belt"; conspicuous pale rings on thin dark abd., pale diamonds less noticeable; dark yellow club looks as if dipped in gold paint; blue-gray eyes; face pale; yellow costa; looks like composite of several other species

female: no club; white belt

habitat: streams, rivers

flight period: April - Nov.

distribution: all but CO

B.M.

Eastern Ringtail
Erpetogomphus designatus

Dustin Huntington

size: large, length 49 - 55 mm, wingspan 64 - 73 mm

male: bright yellow-green striped thorax, no white, isolated dark area on top is totally contained within green area; pale blue eyes; yellow top of first two abdomen segments; pale rings conspicuous along abdomen top, less noticeable pale diamonds; golden club; wing bases have amber wash

female: no club; no white belt

habitat: sandy rivers, streams

flight period: May - October

distribution: NV, CO, AZ, NM

G.L.

Serpent Ringtail
Erpetogomphus lampropeltis

Erpetogomphus lampropeltis natrix - Peter Moulton

size: med/lg, length 41 - 56 mm, wingspan 58 - 72 mm

male: pale yellow rings on abdomen; golden "tail"; no white stripe on thorax; blue eyes; two forms - same abdominal markings but different thoracic pattern and colors:
*E. l. natrix - uninterrupted green markings sides & top of thorax
**E. l. lampropeltis - gray markings thorax; mid-stripe interrupted

female: like male; no club

habitat: streams, rivers

flight period: May - October

distribution: **CA, *AZ, *NM

Erpetogomphus l. lampropeltis R.G.

Russet-tipped Clubtail
Stylurus plagiatus

Robert Behrstock

size: large, length 53 - 66 mm, wingspan 74 - 83 mm

male: long slender abdomen with creamy yellow markings; "club" seg. 8 & 9 yellowish or brown (russet); no rings; legs two-toned; blue eyes; green striped thorax

female: like male; body long, no club; wings may become amber with age

habitat: deep sandy streams, rivers and irrigation ditches in arid regions

flight period: June - November

distribution: so. CA, so. NV, AZ, NM

B.M.

Brimstone Clubtail
Stylurus intricatus

Doug Danforth

size: med/lg, length 41 - 55 mm, wingspan 55 - 64 mm

male: very pale; yellow rings & triangular spots with dark background along abd., rings around segments 3-7 only, yellow club has splayed yellow append. edged with black; yellow head; upper legs yellow; hang-perches on wood, vegetation, not rocks along shoreline

female: similar to male but clubless

habitat: open desert streams/rivers

flight period: June - October

distribution: CA, NV, UT, AZ, NM

G.W.

Olive Clubtail
Stylurus olivaceus

photo rotated 90⁰

Dennis Paulson

size: large, length 56 - 60 mm, wingspan 72 - 74 mm

male: thorax sides tawny gray/olive green with no side stripes; thorax top has tawny treelike mark on black; abd. segments tawny, broadly outlined in black; underside club pale yellow with the top mostly black; appendages black; wings with yellow costa, black veins

female: like male; body long, clubless

habitat: warm, muddy rivers or ponds

flight period: June - September

distribution: CA, NV, UT

D.P.

Sinuous Snaketail
Ophiogomphus occidentis

Robert Behrstock

size: med/lg, length 46 - 52 mm, wingspan 58 - 69 mm

male: yellow-green face with blue eyes; sides of thorax dull olive green with double, dark wavy (sinuous) lines; yellow triangles down abdomen top; club yellow under segments 8-10; five very similar Snaketails occur in the Southwest; compare by shoulder stripe width and shape

female: body more cylindrical

habitat: mt. rivers; lakes

flight period: March - Sept.

distribution: CA, NV, CO?, UT

RAB

Bison Snaketail
Ophiogomphus bison

Robert Behrstock

size: large, length 50 - 51 mm, wingspan 60 - 70 mm

male: thorax bright green; single wide straight dark shoulder stripe (can show very thin green line in middle); black legs; gray-blue eyes; abdomen black with yellow triangles; appendages yellow; forages from the shoreline

female: body more cylindrical, less clubbed; small (bison-like) horns above eyes

habitat: lowland trout streams

flight period: April - October

distribution: CA, NV, UT

C.H.

Arizona/Pale Snaketail
Ophiogomphus arizonicus/O. severus

Rosser Garrison - Pale Snaketail

size: large, length 48 - 55 mm, wingspan 67 - 72 mm

male: very pale coloration; green thorax, black shoulder stripe often completely missing; variable oval spots sides of thorax top; identify by location & append.: ***Arizona**'s lower append. 50% length of uppers; ****Pale**'s 75%

female: body less clubbed; stout

habitat: pools of rocky mt. streams

flight period: May - October

distribution: *Arizona S. - AZ, NM
**Pale S. - CA, NV, UT, CO, NM

D.H.- Pale Snaketail - closeup

Great Basin Snaketail
Ophiogomphus morrisoni

Steve Valley

size: large, length 50 - 52 mm, wingspan 58 - 69 mm

male: green thorax; pale shoulder stripe curved (but not wavy), connected to top pale stripe which is wide & flares near the head, looking somewhat like a pollywog; abdomen has yellow triangles down the top and yellow under clubbed segments; blue eyes; stout yellow appendages

female: less clubbed, stout

habitat: streams in arid lands

flight period: May - August

distribution: CA, NV

S.S.

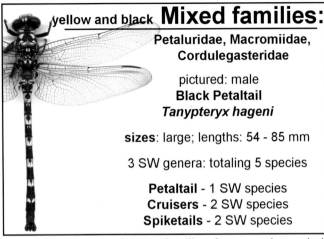

yellow and black # Mixed families:

Petaluridae, Macromiidae, Cordulegasteridae

pictured: male
Black Petaltail
Tanypteryx hageni

sizes: large; lengths: 54 - 85 mm

3 SW genera: totaling 5 species

Petaltail - 1 SW species
Cruisers - 2 SW species
Spiketails - 2 SW species

males: members of these families & genera have dark background color with yellow markings on the thorax and abdomen; compare by appendage shapes & side stripes

females: marked like the males but bodies more stout

habitats: life cycle of 2+ years in rivers, streams, seeps

behaviors: Petaltail flight weak, others very strong fliers

Petaltail - dark eyes do not touch; spots (not stripes) on thorax & abdomen; long stigma; petal-like appendages; nymph semiterrestrial - burrows in seeps; CA & NV (rare)
Cruisers - gray eyes just touch each other; single yellow stripe thorax side; long legs; body arched in powerful flight
Spiketails - tear-shaped blue eyes barely touch each other; thorax - two wide yellow stripes top and each side

Western River Cruiser
Macromia magnifica

Chris Heaivilin

size: very large, length 68 - 74 mm, wingspan 86 - 100

male: pale face; pearly gray eyes touch each other; dark thorax has single yellow side stripe; only half-length stripe on top of thorax; slightly clubbed abdomen has squared yellow spots top, segment 8 spot largest; very long legs.
Bronzed River Cruiser - NM; top thoracic stripe full length

female: like male, not clubbed

habitat: lowlands streams & rivers

flight period: April - September

distribution: CA, NV, UT, AZ

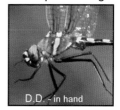

D.D. - in hand

Pacific Spiketail
Cordulegaster dorsalis

Codulegaster dorsalis dorsalis

Kathy Biggs - female   Dave Biggs - male

size: very large, length 70 - 85 mm, wingspan 86 - 105

male: pale face; tear-shaped blue eyes barely touch; dark thorax, two wide yellow stripes top & sides; abd. dark with yellow spots seg. 2-9; powerful flyer; *deserticola (*desert race) more yellow, thin lines between spots

deserticola

D.B.

female: long spikelike ovipositor; dark wing tips; both sexes hang-perch

habitat: hillside sm. wooded streams

flight period: May - October

distribution: *CA, *NV, *UT, CO, NM

Apache Spiketail
Cordulegaster diadema

top view   **Rosser Garrison**   **Doug Danforth** - male

size: very large, length 74 - 88 mm, wingspan 89 - 109

male: very dark appearance; narrowly separated tear-shaped aqua-blue eyes are yellow-green in juveniles; dark abdomen is banded rather than spotted, with segments 6-8 expanded, thin half-ring between bands

female: similar to male; long abdomen with long spike-like ovipositor; both sexes perch by hanging

habitat: small mt. streams with silt bottomed pools

flight period: April - November

distribution: so. UT, AZ, western NM

Damselflies
Zygoptera

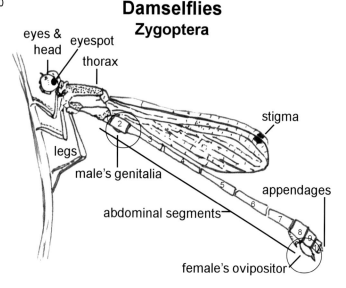

eyes & head

eyespot

thorax

stigma

legs

male's genitalia

2

3

4

5

6

7

8 9

appendages

abdominal segments

female's ovipositor

Slender-bodied, generally smaller and more frail than dragonflies. Most have an eyespot in back of each eye. When perched, all four wings are usually held together alongside or sail-like over the abdomen.
Eyes set far apart on head, appear hammer headed.
Weak fliers, usually found not too far from water.
Males have a bump (genitalia) under their 2nd abdominal segment and four terminal abdominal appendages.
Females have a wide ovipositor on the lower end of their abdomen and only two terminal abdominal appendages.
Damselflies lay their eggs directly into vegetation.
15 SW genera representing 4 of the 5 American families.

Pond Damsels, Coenagrionidae

pictured: male **Northern Bluet**
Enallagma cyathigerum

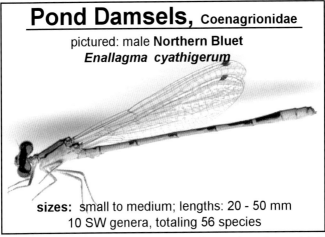

sizes: small to medium; lengths: 20 - 50 mm
10 SW genera, totaling 56 species

males: usually blue and black, a few red, yellow, violet; varying degrees of blue on abdomens; clear wings held alongside or over abdomen when perched, small stigmas

females: abd. more cylindrical; most tan but some blue

habitats: quite variable, still waters, quiet streams

behaviors: wings held closed when perched; low flying

Bluets, *Enallagma*: perch on vegetation; wings at rest alongside abdomen; tandem oviposit at still water sites
Dancers, *Argia*: "dancing" flight; perch on ground and/or rocks with wings held above abdomen; tandem oviposit in moving waters; territorial wing clapping; long spines on legs
Forktails, *Ischnura*: mostly black; blue on thorax & near abd. tip; perch on emergent vegetation; nontandem oviposit into floating vegetation; resting wing position variable

Northern/Boreal/Alkali Bluet
Enallagma cyathigerum/E. boreale/ E. clausum

Northern Bluet - **Doug Aguillard**

size: medium, length 29 - 40 mm

male: third segment more than 50% blue; side stripe is undivided with a jag near the front; large blue eyespots; lower append. longer than uppers. **Alkali** has thin side stripe; found alkali water. Identify 3 to species by append. shape using hand lens, see p.98

female

R.B. - Boreal

female: much less blue, or tan and black

habitat: No./Bo. - cool still or slow water

flight periods: April - October

distribution: all SW; Alkali not in AZ

Familiar Bluet
Enallagma civile

Sept. 24, 2005

Arivaca Cienega

Steve Potter

size: medium, length 28 - 39 mm

male: markings more blue than black, third segment more than 50% blue; top thorax stripe dark; small comma-shaped eyespots; top appendages longer than lowers, large and finlike with pale "button," appear splayed; see appendage illustrations, p.98. Bluets fly low over water along shoreline.

female: like male or tan and black

habitat: still waters with fields

flight period: all year in south

distribution: all Southwest

J.L.

River Bluet
Enallagma anna

Robert Behrstock

size: medium, length 29 - 36 mm

male: middle abdominal segments about half-blue from above; appendages slightly forked; uppers noticeably longer than lowers, with the top fork extending well beyond lower appendages and angled downward (without a pale button on end) - noticeable to the naked eye

female: pale areas blue or tan

habitat: slow streams, ditches

flight period: April - Sept.

distribution: all SW but AZ

RAB

Tule/Arroyo Bluet
Enallagma carunculatum/E. praevarum

Tule - Robert Behrstock

size: small/medium, length 26 - 37 mm

male: segments 3-8 more black than blue; 3rd seg. more than 50% black; segs. 8 & 9 blue; thorax top stripe dark.
Tule Bluet - large pale button tip of upper appendages.
Arroyo Bluet (not pictured) - forked upper appendages.
See p.98 for illustrations of *Enallagma* appendages.

female: pale areas blue or tan; no blue on tail

habitat: lakes, ponds, streams

flight period: Feb. - Dec.

distribution: all Southwest

Tule - P.H.

Double-striped Bluet
Enallagma basidens

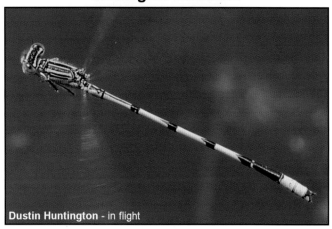

Dustin Huntington - in flight

size: small, length 21 - 28 mm

male: thin blue line middle of dark side stripes (doubled); thin blue line middle of top dark thoracic stripe; tiny blue eyespots connected by thin line; blue on segments 8-9, only on sides of segment 10; black appendages

female: like male but paler or tan; segment 10 all pale

habitat: ponds, lakes, ditches

flight period: March - November

distribution: CA, CO, AZ, NM

RAB

Taiga Bluet
Coenagrion resolutum

Nick Donnelly

size: small, length 27 - 31 mm

male: mostly black above, with pale blue to turquoise markings; green tinged thorax; middle abd. segs. mostly black, black markings seg. 2 U-shaped; tear-shaped eyespots

female: turquoise, tan, or green; very large eyespots

habitat: slow waters in northern mts; prefers still, shaded water

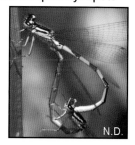

N.D.

flight period: April - August

distribution: CA, UT, CO, AZ

Bluet appendages

Enallagma male abdominal appendages

Sometimes it is necessary to have a Bluet in hand and examine its terminal appendages using a hand lens to make a final identification. Side and 45% views:

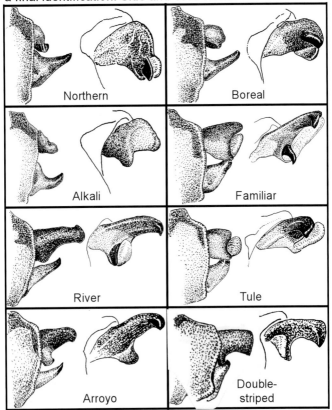

Northern

Boreal

Alkali

Familiar

River

Tule

Arroyo

Double-striped

California/Aztec Dancer
A. nahuana/Argia agrioides

Greg Lasley - Aztec Dancer

size: small/medium, length 23 - 37 mm

male: brilliant sky-blue; thorax shoulder stripe variably forked (lower stripe can be interrupted); blue "tail" seg. 8-10; ***CA's** distance between lower append. from above greater than width of individual append.; ****Aztec's** not so.

female: less colorful, thicker bodied than male; one form like male; other is tan and black

habitat: open rivers and streams

flight period: March - November

distribution: *CA, *NV, *AZ; **all SW

H.H. - California Dancer

Vivid Dancer
Argia vivida

Rosser Garrison

size: medium, length 29 - 41 mm

male: vivid blue & black markings; thorax top stripe has wide urn shape; side thoracic stripe pinched at mid-length; middle abdomen segment sides have small triangular black streaks; blue tip surrounds seg. 8-10; when cool coloring becomes more violet; immatures - milky gray

female: tan/gray & black or male-like

habitat: seeps, streams; wanders

flight period: January - November

distribution: all Southwest

RAB

Springwater Dancer
Argia plana

Roy Beckemeyer

size: medium, length 33 - 40 mm

male: like **Vivid Dancer** but more violet (AZ, western NM) or blue (eastern NM); found south of where **Vivid** is found; differentiated from **Vivid** & also similar **Apache Dancer** (UT, AZ, NM), by slightly wider, more rounded upper appendages (visible under hand lens); see p.114

female: like male or pale browns

habitat: canopied streams, seeps

flight period: March - November

distribution: CO, AZ, NM

RAB

Emma's Dancer
Argia emma

Chris Heaivilin

size: medium, length 32 - 40 mm

male: purplish species; occurs further north than **Tonto**; thoracic side stripe pinched at middle; black stripe top of thorax unique - very narrow & straight; abdomen lavender and black with no side triangles; pale stigma; see p.114

female: male-like or yellowish tan; top thoracic stripe very thin

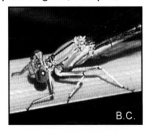

B.C.

habitat: rocky streams, rivers

flight period: March - Oct.

distribution: CA, NV, UT, CO

Tonto Dancer
Argia tonto

Doug Danforth

size: medium, length 39 - 44 mm

male: violet or purple species; narrow top thoracic stripe; large eyespots; back of head pale; dark shoulder stripe pinched, not forked, lower end abruptly wider than upper end; abdomen with no dark side streaks on sides; tail-tip violet; range is south of **Emma's Dancer**'s; append. p.114

female: like male, color usually tan; top stripe a bit wider

habitat: wooded mt. streams

flight period: May - Sept.

distribution: AZ, sw. NM

RAB

Variable Dancer
Argia fumipennis

Rosser Garrison

size: medium, length 29 - 34 mm

male: violet when mature; thoracic shoulder stripe forked; top stripe wide & straight; lower half of thorax without contrasting white; "tail" is violet with black under 8-10; in SW slightly smoky wings; prefers slow moving areas of streams

female: like male but light brown or tan with wide black stripe on abdomen side

habitat: slow streams, ponds

flight period: March - Nov.

distribution: CO, AZ, NM

R.G.

Lavender Dancer
Argia hinei

Doug Aguillard

size: small/med, length 30 - 35 mm

male: violet when mature; thoracic shoulder stripe forked; frontal stripe wide; mature males show lower half of thorax pruinose white; seg. 8-10 form contrasting blue "tail" with black under 8 & 9 only; prefers shallow rocky stream areas

female: light brown; abd. & thorax patterning similar to male; dark intrusions on pale tail tip

habitat: streams (even ephemeral)

flight period: March - November

distribution: CA, NV, AZ, NM

RAB

Kiowa Dancer
Argia immunda

Greg Lasley

size: small/medium, length 26 - 38 mm

male: blue or blue violet & black; pale thoracic side stripe wide and irregular in shape; dark side stripe forked; large eyespots; abd. seg. 3-6 unique with thin pale basal ring & then 3 alternating black-pale-black markings each of approximately the same width; wings clear, dark veins

female: tan where male is blue

habitat: streams & rivers, lakes

flight period: April - November

distribution: CA, NV, AZ, NM

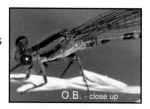

O.B. - close up

Paiute Dancer
Argia alberta

Doug Danforth

size: small/medium, length 26 - 32 mm

male: small, dark for a dancer; dark thoracic shoulder stripe prominent and forked; small eye-spots; wings clear, dark veins; abdomen mostly dark with contrasting blue or grayish purple rings that don't close at the top, middle segments black on top; immatures colored more violet

female: light brown & black

habitat: stream/pond arid areas

flight period: April - November

distribution: all Southwest

S.S. - close up

Amethyst Dancer
Argia pallens

Steve Krotzer

size: medium, length 32 - 35 mm

male: mostly violet & very pale, even eyes & legs; top thoracic stripe thin & narrow, dark side stripe very thin and pinched at middle; prothorax ("neck") violet; pale stigma; no triangles down side of abdomen; segment 7 pale, not black

female: like male or brown where male is violet

habitat: small streams

flight period: March - Nov.

distribution: AZ, NM

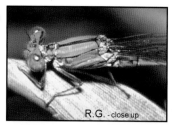

R.G. - close up

Dusky Dancer
Argia translata

Steve Krozter

---

size: medium, length 32 - 38 mm

male: thin; dark gunmetal blue coloration; side dark stripe can disappear with age; abdomen very dark with pale rings; no blue "tail"; top of eyes purple; wings clear or slightly smoky; lower thorax becomes dark pruinose; black legs.
Tezpi - (AZ, NM) even darker, metallic thorax; wings golden

female: like male or tan; segments 8-10 pale side stripe

habitat: open streams, rivers

flight period: March - Nov.

distribution: AZ, NM

J.A.

Sooty Dancer
Argia lugens

Rosser Garrison

size: medium, length 40 - 50 mm

male: large for a damselfly; unlike most Dancers, no blue near abdomen tip; thorax develops dark sooty blue pruinosity; noticeable pale ring around each segment; dark eyes; dark wing veins can become slightly smoky; perches on rocks; immature patterned brown like female

female: thorax patterned blue or brown; pale rings abd.

habitat: rocky streams, rivers

flight period: April - October

distribution: CA, UT, CO, AZ, NM

O.B.

Powdered Dancer
Argia moesta

Steve Potter

size: medium, length 37 - 43 mm

male: large for a damselfly; develops chalky/powdery white/gray pruinosity with age, especially thorax; abdomen turns pale gray on segments 8-10; compare immature males and females with **Blue-fronted Dancer**

female: pale blue or light brown thorax; older females sometimes become a bit pruinose

habitat: rocky rivers, windy lakes

flight period: February - Nov.

distribution: all SW states

G.L.

Blue-fronted Dancer
Argia apicalis

Steve Krotzer

size: medium, length 33 - 40 mm

male: bright blue thorax, top and shoulder stripes very thin; blue face; clear wings; black abdomen, segments 8-10 blue; small brown stigma; dark eyes, tiny eyespots; compare to similar immature **Powdered Dancer**

female: same markings; can be colored male-like or rusty brown

habitat: muddy rivers & lakes

flight period: March - October

distribution: CO, AZ, NM

D.D.

Blue-ringed Dancer
Argia sedula

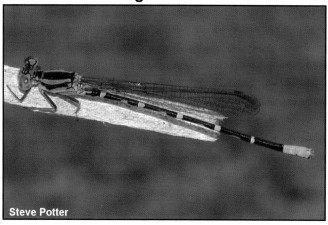

Steve Potter

size: medium, length 29 - 34 mm

male: black abdomen has narrow blue rings separating sections; blue "tail" 8-10; thorax has wide dark side and top stripe; wings dark veined, amber tinged

female: always paler than male, showing olive-tan wherever male is blue; wings amber-tinged

habitat: sunny sections of small/medium rivers

flight period: March - Nov.

distribution: all Southwest

O.B.

Dancer appendages
Argia male abdominal appendages

Sometimes it is necessary to have a Dancer in hand and examine its terminal appendages using a 10X⁺ hand lens to make a final identification. Dorsal and lateral views:

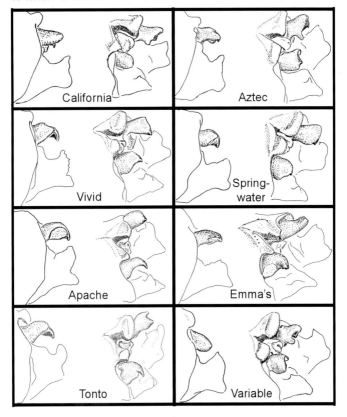

California

Aztec

Vivid

Spring-water

Apache

Emma's

Tonto

Variable

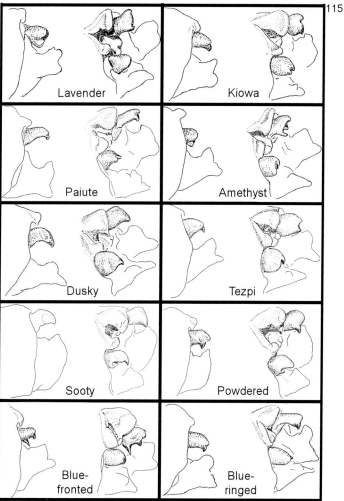

Lavender

Kiowa

Paiute

Amethyst

Dusky

Tezpi

Sooty

Powdered

Blue-
fronted

Blue-
ringed

Fiery-eyed Dancer
Argia oenea

Rosser Garrison

size: medium, length 33 - 39 mm

male: upper eyes bright red, blue wash back of the eye; coppery orange face; top of thorax dark metallic coppery red; abd. segments 3-6 violet (or blue) above with blue (or violet) "tail" segments 8-10; dark legs; clear wings

female: like male or brown; no red; pale "island" in midst of dark side stripe

habitat: streams and rivers

flight period: May - November

distribution: AZ

R.G.

Painted Damsel
Hesperagrion heterodoxum

Nick Donnelly

size: medium, length 27 - 35 mm

male: red eye spots; red top seg. 8-10; yellow under segments 1-7; 4 blue marks thorax top, sides blue, yellow brown in immature; like no other Southwestern damselfly; coloration variable by age - immature all orange

female: blue tail only top seg. 7; thorax top - blue triangles; similar to **Plain's Forktail**

habitat: creeks and streams

flight period: March - Nov.

distribution: CO, AZ, NM

P.M. - imm.

P.M.

Western Red Damsel
Amphiagrion abbreviatum

Rod Miller

size: very small, length 23 - 28 mm

male: stocky; hairy black head and thorax, brown eyes, black on top; bright red abdomen barely extends beyond wings; black top and/or sides segments 7-10; dark legs

female: stout; pale peach to reddish; thorax tawny; rare dark pruinose form exists

habitat: mountain lakes, marshes, slow streams

flight period: April - Sept.

distribution: all Southwest

Desert Firetail
Telebasis salva

Peter Moulton

size: very small, length 23 - 29 mm

male: dainty and slender; all red abdomen extends well beyond wing tips; red face and eyes; black eye spots; thorax red with black; red legs; tip of abd. without black

female: some black thorax top; eggs laid in algae mats

habitat: shallow waters with algae scum; lowlands (not just in deserts)

flight period: Mar. - Dec.

distribution: all SW, except CO

D.D.

Rambur's Forktail
Ischnura ramburii

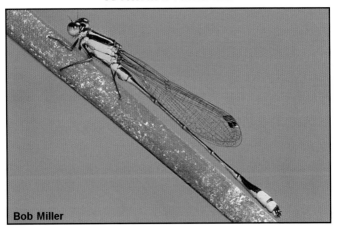

Bob Miller

size: medium, length 27 - 36 mm

male: green-blue shoulder stripe very thin, parallel sided; tiny circular eyespots; thorax and seg. 1-3 greenish-blue; yellowish-orange underside only of seg. 3-7; blue surrounds seg. 8, part of 9, not 10; lower append. point straight out

female: male-like or Day-Glo red/orange turning tan/ olive; wide black stripe thorax top

habitat: pond/lake/slow streams

flight period: March - Dec.

distribution: CA, NV, AZ, NM

D.M.

Desert Forktail
Ischnura barberi

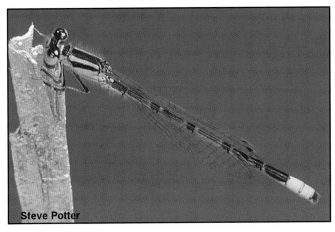

Steve Potter

size: medium, length 27 - 35 mm

male: pale shoulder stripe thicker than **Rambur's**, widest near eyes; large tear-shaped eyespots connected by a line; pale orange on mid segs. curves partly up & over the abd. leaving the dark areas on top appearing dart shaped; blue surrounds all of segs. 8 & 9; lower append. point upward

female: like male or pale tan-orange; narrow top stripe

habitat: pond/lakes/slow streams

flight period: March - November

distribution: CA, NV, UT, AZ, NM

O.B.

Citrine Forktail
Ischnura hastata

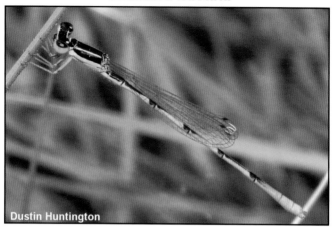

Dustin Huntington

size: very small, length 20 - 27 mm

male: abdomen (even tip) mostly yellow above & below with some black; thoracic stripes green; forewing - pale reddish-brown stigma that is NOT touching the leading edge; hind wing has (usual) dark stigma

female: imm. orange & black with seg. 1-4 mostly orange; mature - pale pruinose

RAB

habitat: marshes/ponds/streams

flight period: all year (in South)

distribution: CA, NV, CO, AZ, NM

D.H.

Eastern/Mexican/Western Forktail
Ischnura verticalis/ I. demorsa/ I. perparva

Chris Heaivilin - Western

---

size: small, **length 21 - 33 mm**

male: thorax sides & top - blue-green stripes; noticeable fine pale rings across each dark abd. segment; blue tip has dark intrusions on sides; CA & NV assume Western; elsewhere differentiate by appendages

female: imm. orange & black with segs. 1-3 mostly orange; becomes pale pruinose

K.W. - Western

habitat: weedy ponds, creeks

flight period: Feb. - Nov.

distribution: see checklist

R.G. - Mexican

Pacific/Plains Forktail
Ischnura cervula/I. damula

Rosser Garrison - Plains

RAB - Pacific (imm. female)

size: small, **length 22 - 34 mm**

male: abdomen black with blue "tail" markings that touch top & bottom; black thorax top - 4 tiny blue spots, 1 each "corner"; thorax sides blue; use append. chart p.126

female: stripes on top of thorax; shows pinkish-orange eyespot color as immature; becomes all dark pruinose when mature; pale stigma; male-like form has larger dots

habitat: weedy ponds & creeks

flight period: all year in south

distribution: see checklist p.158

C.H.   Pacific (mature. female)

Black-fronted Forktail
Ischnura denticollis

Chris Heaivilin

size: very small, **length 22 - 26 mm**

male: no stripes or dots on top of thorax; all dark above, sides of thorax blue (green in immature); blue patches on top & bottom segs. 8-9 do not touch; chartreuse underside; frail; top appendages bent down. **SF Forktail**, rare, CA's Bay Area, lower append. not as hooked/noticeable

female: imm. - pale coral; mature green/blue thorax sides

habitat: lakes, ponds, seeps

flight period: all year in so.

distribution: all Southwest

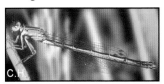

C.H

Forktail appendages
Ischnura male abdominal appendages

Examine forktail in hand using a hand lens
and terminal appendages illustrations to
make a final identification. 45⁰ views:

forktail larva

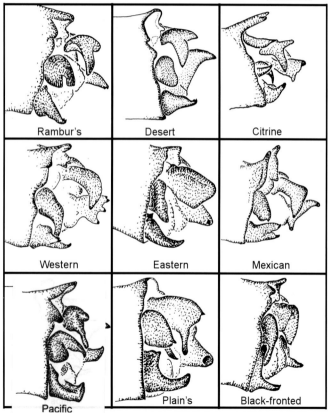

Rambur's	Desert	Citrine
Western	Eastern	Mexican
Pacific	Plain's	Black-fronted

Spreadwings, Lestidae

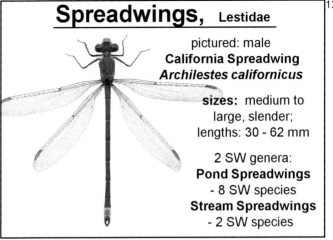

pictured: male
California Spreadwing
Archilestes californicus

sizes: medium to large, slender; lengths: 30 - 62 mm

2 SW genera:
Pond Spreadwings
- 8 SW species
Stream Spreadwings
- 2 SW species

males: dark with blues, greens; blue eyes; pruinose pale area near tip; some show more extensive pruinosity

females: more stout; less colorful; not pruinose

habitats: ponds, marshes, streams, slow rivers

behaviors: often hold wings open when at rest, à la stealth bombers; oviposit in plant tissue that is above water level

Pond Spreadwings, *Lestes*: found flying at still water sites summer through fall; patrol shoreline from emergent vegetation on which they rest; oviposit while in tandem into non-woody vegetation above the water level

Stream Spreadwings, *Archilestes*: moving water sites; SW's largest damselflies; tandem oviposit into woody vegetation such as bay, alder & willow branches overhanging creeks/sm. rivers (even when dry); late season flight

Common Spreadwing
Lestes disjunctus

Ray Bruun

size: medium, slender, length 30 - 40 mm

male: blue eyes; thorax becomes pruinose pale blue; first two and last two or three abdominal seg. become pruinose gray-blue; other segments have dark/green sheen; lower appendages long & straight but may be held crossed or like a V (examine carefully with hand lens); black stigma

female: more stout; no pruinosity

habitat: weedy ponds, streams

flight period: April - November

distribution: all Southwest

O.B.

Spotted/Lyre-tipped Spreadwing
Lestes congener/ L. unguiculatus

Lyre-tip. append.

D.M.

Ray Bruun - Spotted Spreadwing

size: medium, slender, length 31 - 42 mm

male: blue eyes; thorax dark; first & last two abdominal segments pruinose gray-blue; other segments - dark or green sheen; ***Spotted** - short lower appendages <50% of uppers; 4 dark spots thorax underside; dark brown stigma ****Lyre-tipped** - lower append. lyre-shaped; stigma - pale tips

female: more stout; less colorful

habitat: weedy ponds, streams

flight period: April - November

distribution: *all SW **see p.156

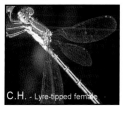

C.H. - Lyre-tipped female

Plateau Spreadwing
Lestes alacer

Greg Lasley

size: medium, slender, length 34 - 45 mm

male: broad dark stripe top of thorax, dark side stripe variable width; abdomen slender, esp. middle segments; reduced dark markings abd. top; segments 1 & 2, 8 -10 become pruinose with age; lower appen. 75% of uppers

female: similar to male

habitat: grass-edged ponds, slow streams at low elevations

flight period: January - Nov.

distribution: AZ, NM

RAB

Emerald Spreadwing
Lestes dryas

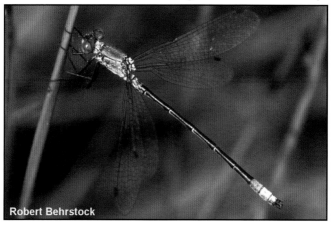

Robert Behrstock

size: medium, slender, length 32 - 40 mm

male: top of thorax bright metallic green; sides of thorax blue; abdomen bright metallic green; first two and last two segments can show blue; appendages are long and broad at the end. **Black Spreadwing** - CA, very similar except black not green coloration; bronzy thorax

female: stocky; less emerald

habitat: forested mt. areas

flight period: April - Oct.

distribution: all Southwest

G.D.

California Spreadwing
Archilestes californicus

Ray Braun

---

size: medium/large, slender, length 42- 59 mm

male: long body brown &/or black with pruinose area near tip; 2 incomplete white stripes thorax sides; blue eyes; wings colorless, pale stigma; upper appendages semicircular, lower are parallel; late season flier

female: less colorful brown tones

habitat: streams with alders/willows

flight period: June - November

distribution: CA, NV, AZ

TWD - ovipositing pair

Great Spreadwing
Archilestes grandis

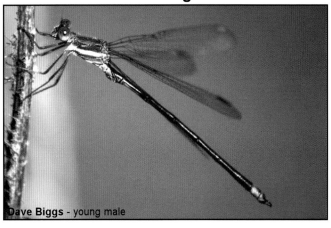

Dave Biggs - young male

---

size: large, slender, length 50 - 62 mm

male: long body grey with greenish sheen, pruinose area near tip; one continuous pale side stripe on thorax (yellow in mature); blue eyes; dark stigma; top append. semicircular, lowers divergent; North Am.'s largest damselfly; late season flier

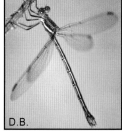

D.B.

female: less colorful

habitat: streams with alders/willows

flight period: March - January

distribution: CA, UT, CO, AZ, NM

Broad-winged Damsels,

Calopterygidae

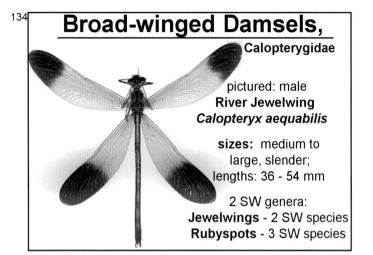

pictured: male
River Jewelwing
Calopteryx aequabilis

sizes: medium to large, slender; lengths: 36 - 54 mm

2 SW genera:
Jewelwings - 2 SW species
Rubyspots - 3 SW species

males: large for damselflies; colorful patches in wings

females: more stout; less colorful bodies and wings

habitats: streams, slow rivers, esp. with vegetation

behaviors: butterfly-like courtship &/or male display flights; perch horizontally, head down on vegetation, shoreline rocks

Jewelwings, *Calopteryx*: large broad wings with black wing coloration either at tip of or for entire wing; beautiful green and blue iridescent coloration on body changes with angle of viewing; long spindly legs; courtship displays
Rubyspots, *Hetaerina*: males have basal quarter to third of wings with beautiful red patches; thorax matures to red as seen through smoky glass or to dark with reddish iridescence; very long dark legs; males duel in display flights

River Jewelwing
Calopteryx aequabilis

Netta Smith

size: medium, length 43 - 54 mm

male: jewellike bright metallic green/blue thorax and abdomen; outer 1/3 of wings conspicuously black; in CO the **Ebony Jewelwing** has wings of both sexes all dark

female: duller abdomen, pale tip; smoky wings have a contrasting pale stigma; may oviposit under water

habitat: fast waters of large wooded streams/rivers; larva live in root masses

N.S.

flight period: May - August

distribution: CA, NV, UT, CO

American Rubyspot
Hetaerina americana

Bob Miller

size: medium/lg, **length 36 - 51 mm**

male: wings ruby red basal 1/3 to 1/2; thorax blood red as if under black glass, pale side stripes; abd. bronzy brown-green with thin rings; CA usually no stigma, other states pale stigma. **Smoky Rubyspot**, NM - wings mostly dark

female: less colorful; wing patches orangish, streak leading edge, tips mostly clear

habitat: open streams, rivers

flight period: February - Dec.

distribution: all Southwest

R.B.

Canyon Rubyspot
Hetaerina vulnerata

Doug Danforth

size: medium/lg, length 36 - 49 mm

male: red at wing base usually less extensive than **Am. Rubyspot**'s; smoky edge/wing-tip; no stigma; compare by append. **American** - upper appendages 1-2 toothlike lobes inside at midpoint; **Canyon** lacks these lobes

female: less colorful; wing patches orangish, no stigma, smoky wing tips

A.J.

habitat: canopied streams, rivers

flight period: March - November

distribution: UT, AZ, NM

Credits:

Thanks to **Dave Biggs, Robert Behrstock, Terri Gallion** and **Nancy Bauer** for their valuable editorial help and layout suggestions. Very special thanks go to **Rosser Garrison** and **Natalia von Ellenrieder** for all of their many valuable suggestions and thorough review of the factual content and especially for their considerable help on the Dancers (*Argia*) section and the damselfly appendages drawings.

Sandy Upson, Richard Bailowitz, Douglas Danforth & Ann Johnson of SE AZ and Robert Larsen & Karen Gains in NM have added greatly to the knowledge of dragonflies of the Southwest, thanks!

Photo & Illustrations Credits:

Without the work of the talented, patient photographers and illustrators listed below, this guide could not exist and I am forever grateful. Scans & photos not listed in following are by the author.   t=top b=bottom m=middle l=left r=right

Illustrations -

Barbara Chasteen: 10, 90   **Rosser Garrison:** 98, 114, 115
Natalia von Ellenrieder: 126

Photos -

John Abbott: 109b
Doug Aguillard: 92t, 105t
Steve Abbott: 16b
Robert A. Behrstock (RAB): 15tb, 17b, 19tb, 23t, 38t, 43t, 48t, 49b, 74b, 75t, 79t, 82tb, 83t, 94tb, 95t, 96b, 100b, 101b, 103b, 105b, 122m, 124m, 130b, 131t
Roy Beckemeyer: 101t

Dave Biggs (D.B.): back cover, 28t, 32tb, 63r, 66l, 76t, 88rb, 133tb
Omar Bocanegra: 13t, 60l, 106b, 110b, 113b, 121b, 128b
David Bozsik: 16t
Ray Bruun (R.B.): 17t, 22tb, 24b, 37b, 41b, 51b, 53b, 63l, 64l, 65lr, 66r, 92b, 128t, 129t, 132t, 136b

Steven Bruun: 36t

Bob Claypole: 59l, 102b

Doug Danforth: 47b, 61l, 69lrb, 73t, 80t, 87b, 89r, 103t, 107t, 112b, 119b, 137t

T.W. Davies @ California Academy of Sciences: 132b

George P. Doerksen @ Royal BC Museum: 20t, 51t, 52tb, 131b

Nick Donnelly: 20b, 97tb, 117t

Rosser Garrison: 30t, 57t, 78b, 84t, 89l, 100t, 104tb, 108b, 110t, 116tb, 123b, 124t

Heather Hacking: 99b

Pete Haggard: 64r, 70b, 95b

Chris Heaivilin: 59r, 62rl, 83b, 87t, 102t, 118b, 123t, 124b, 125tb, 129b

Matt Heindel: 28b

David Hofmann (D.Ho.): 35b

Dustin Huntington (D.H.): 25t, 30b, 38b, 39t, 46t, 77t, 84b, 96t, 122tb

Ann Johnson: 67lrb, 68lr, 137b

Steve Krotzer: 108t, 109t, 112t

Greg Lasley: 21tb, 27t, 33t, [139] 36b, 40t, 45t, 77b, 99t, 106t, 111b, 130t

James Lasswell: 93b

Ron LeValley: 61r

Dave McShaffrey: 27b, 34b, 42tb, 120b, 129m

Bob Miller: 33b, 60r, 76b, 79b, 120t, 136t

Rod Miller: 14b, 26b, 29b, 35t, 37t, 53t, 56b, 71lrb, 73b, 118t

Peter Moulton: 26t, 49t, 74t, 78t, 117mb, 119t

Dennis Paulson: 56t, 62b, 68b, 81tb

Bob Parks: front cover, 14t, 25b, 31t, 70t

Steve Potter: 12b, 24t, 41t, 44t, 93t, 111t, 113t, 121t

Netta Smith: 135tb

Susan Steele: 85b, 107b

Steve Valley: 85t

Gordon Warrick: 46b, 80b

David Westover: 18t, 23b, 29t, 50tb

Alan Wight: 34t, 47t

Curtis Williams: 13b, 31b, 43b, 48b, 55tb, 75b

Ken Wilson: 39b, 123m

William Zittrich: 12t, 40t

Glossary

abdomen   (abd.) last part of the dragonfly body, which is long, slender and has 10 segments.

Anisoptera   scientific name for the suborder to which the dragonflies (not damselflies) belong.

appendages   (append.) additional extensions coming from the tip of the dragonfly/damselfly abdomen: females have two, male dragonflies have three; male damselflies have four.   Distinct for each species.

costa   leading edge (vein) of wing.

damselfly   member of the suborder Zygoptera. Small, less robust than dragonflies. Narrow wings held sail-like over or alongside back, eyes widely separated.

dragonfly*   member of the suborder Anisoptera. Large and robust with bulky body. Wings held out flat at sides, the eyes usually touching.
  * However, this word is often used for both dragonflies and damselflies, including <u>all</u> members of the order Odonata.

emerge   to come out of the water and then out of the exuvia and become an adult flying dragonfly.

endemic   confined to a certain region.

exuvia, (pl. exuviae)   the cast skin left behind by a dragonfly nymph when it either molts between nymph stages or emerges as an adult dragonfly.

genitalia   reproductive organs, external sexual organs.

habitat   environment in which the flying dragonfly and especially the nymph can be found.

hind wing (HW) anal triangle   group of 2-3 cells at the base of male hind wing that varies in shape among species of darners.

instar   a larval stage. Most dragonflies go through 11-13.

labium   the lower lip;in nymph specialized to seize prey.

larva, (pl) larvae   nymph; immature stage between the egg and flying adult. Dragonfly larvae usually live under water.

genus, (pl) genera   classification level between family and species; a genus includes a group of related species.

nodus   crossvein at slight bend in dragonfly wing, at midpoint of front edge.

Odonata   scientific name for the order to which all dragonflies and damselflies belong.

oviposit   to lay eggs.

prothorax   front division of thorax bearing the first pair of legs.

pruinose/pruinosity   powdery covering that develops on some dragonfly species, mostly on males, turning them a light blue, gray or white color as they mature.

stigma   small colored thickened area of wing, rectangular shaped on front edge near tip.

thorax   the part of the dragonfly's body between the head and abdomen to which the wings and legs are attached.

venation   arrangement of veins in the wings of the dragonfly.

Zygoptera   scientific name for suborder to which the damselflies (not dragonflies) belong.

Bibliography and References

Abbott, John C., in press. *Dragonflies and Damselflies of the South-central United States*. Princeton University Press. 2000. "Odonata Central, South-central United States" <http://www.esb.utexas.edu/jcabbott/odonata>

Biggs, Kathy, 2004. "California Dragonflies & Damselflies, aka California Odonata." <http://www.sonic.net/dragonfly/> 2000. *Common Dragonflies of California, A Beginner's Pocket Guide*. Azalea Creek Publishing.

Cannings, Robert A., 2002. *Introducing the Dragonflies of British Columbia and the Yukon*. Royal British Columbia Museum. 1995. "Diagrammatic Key: Aeshnidae." <http://rbcm1.rbcm.gov.bc.ca/nh_papers/aeshna_key/dragonf1.htm>

Corbet, Phillip, 1999. *Dragonflies: Behavior and Ecology of Odonata*. Cornel Universisty Press.

Dunkle, Sidney W., 2000. *Dragonflies through Binoculars*. Oxford University Press.

Herman, Karen J., 1998. "New Mexico Dragonfly Notebook." <http://www.rt66.com/~kjherman/odonata/notebook.html>

Huntington, Dustin, 2003. *The Common Dragonflies of Bitter-lake National Wildlife Refuge*. Imunu. 2003. *The Common Dragonflies of New Mexico*. DVD - Imunu

Lyons, Ron, 1997. "Checklist of the Odonata of California." <http://uci.net/~pondhawk/odonata/odonata_calif.html> 1998. "Damsels and Dragons - the Insect Order Odonata." <http://uci.net/~pondhawk/odonata/ips_odonata.html>

Johnson, Ann., 2002. "Arizona Odonata."
   <http://www.hologrambirds.com/Arizona/main/default.asp>

Manolis, Timothy D., 2003. *Dragonflies and Damselflies of California*. The University of California Press.

Mauffray, Bill, 1998. "Dragonflies and Damselflies (Odonata Information Network)." <http://www.afn.org/~iori/>

Needham, James, Westfall, Minter, Michael May, 2000. *The Dragonflies of North America*. UC Press, Berkeley.

Nikula, Blair, Sones, Jackie, 2002. *Stokes Beginner's Guide to Dragonflies & Damselflies*, Little, Brown & Co., New York.

Oswald, John D., 2001. "Tiara Biodiversity Project. Odonata:" <http://www.csdl.tamu.edu/tiara/>

Paulson, Dennis, 1999. "Dragonfly (Odonata) Biodiversity" <http://www.ups.edu/biology/museum/UPSdragonflies.html> Slater Museum Natural History, University of Puget Sound. 1999. *Dragonflies of Washington*, Seattle Audubon Society

Paulson, Dennis R., and Dunkle, Sid. W., 1996. "Common Names of North American Dragonflies and Damselflies," "ARGIA", vol. 8, No. 2. Dragonfly Society of the Americas .

von Ellenrieder, N., 2003. "A synopsis of the Neotropical species of '*Aeshna*' Fabricius: The genus *Rhionaeschna* Förster (Odonata: Aeshnidae). Tijdschrift voor Entomologie 146: 67-207."

Westfall, Minter and May, Michael, 1996. *The Damselflies of North America*. Scientific Publishers, Gainesville.

Index

Checklist of the Dragonflies and Damselflies of the South West

Bold dark text = a dragonfly pictured in Com. Dragonflies of SW

Non-bold dark = a dragonfly mentioned in Com. Dragonflies of SW

Non-bold gold text = a dragonfly not common in SW, not included

* = pictured/mentioned in Com. Dragonflies of CA   ? = unconfirmed

COMMON NAME	SCIENTIFIC NAME	STATE					
DRAGONFLIES	ANISOPTERA	CA	NV	UT	CO	AZ	NM
SKIMMERS	LIBELLLULIDAE						
Red-tailed Pennant	***Brachymesia furcata***	X				X	
Four-spotted Pennant	*B. gravida*					X	X
Pale-faced Clubskim.*	***Brechmorhoga mendax***	X	X	X		X	X
Masked Clubskm.	*B. pertinax*					X	
Halloween Pennant	*Celithemis eponina*				X		X
Banded Pennant	*C. fasciata*						X
Checkered Setwing	***Dythemis fugax***					X	X
Mayan Setwing	*D. maya*					X	
Black Setwing	*D. nigrescens*					X	X
Swift Setwing	*D. velox*					X	X
Western Pondhawk*	***Erythemis collocata***	X	X	X	X	X	X
Eastern Pondhawk	***E. simplicicollis***				X	X	X
Great Pondhawk	***E. vesiculosa***				X	X	X
Plateau Dragonlet	***Erythrodiplax basifusca***					X	X
Seaside Dragonlet	*E. berenice*						X
Black-winged Dragonlet	*E. funerea*					X	
Boreal Whiteface	*Leucorrhinia borealis*			X	X		
Crimson-rng. Whiteface*	***L. glacialis***	X	X				
Hudsonian Whiteface*	***L. hudsonica***	X	X	X	X		
Dot-tailed Whiteface*	***L. intacta***	X	X	X	X		X
Red-waisted Whiteface	***L. proxima***	X		X	X		
Comanche Skimmer	***Libellula comanche***	X	X	X		X	X

COMMON NAME	SCIENTIFIC NAME	CA	NV	UT	CO	AZ	NM
DRAGONFLIES	**ANISOPTERA**						
Bleached Skimmer	*L. composita*	X	X	X	?	X	X
Neon Skimmer	*L. croceipennis*	X				X	X
8-spotted Skimmer*	*L. forensis*	X	X	X	X	X	X
Chalk-fronted Corporal	*L. julia*	X					
Widow Skimmer*	*L. luctuosa*	X	X	X	X	X	X
Common Whitetail*	*L. lydia*	X	X	X	X	X	X
Hoary Skimmer*	*L. nodisticta*	X	X	X	X	X	X
12-spotted Skimmer*	*L. puchella*	X	X	X	X	X	X
4-spotted Skimmer*	*L. quadrimaculata*	X	X	X	X	X	X
Flame Skimmer*	*L. saturata*	X	X	X	X	X	X
Desert Whitetail	*L. subornata*	X	X	X	X	X	X
Marl Pennant	*Macrodiplax balteata*	X				X	X
Straw-colored Sylph	*Macrothemis inacuta*					X	
Orange-bellied Skimmer	*Orthemis discolor*					X	
Roseate Skimmer	*O. ferruginea*	X	X	X	X	X	X
Blue Dasher*	*Pachydiplax longipennis*	X	X	X	X	X	X
Red Rock Skimmer*	*Paltothemis lineatipes*	X		X		X	X
Wandering Glider*	*Pantala flavescens*	X	X	X	X	X	X
Spot-winged Glider*	*P. hymenaea*	X	X	X	X	X	X
Slough Amberwing	*Perithemis domitia*					X	
Mexican Amberwing*	*P. intensa*	X	X			X	X
Eastern Amberwing	*P. tenera*				X	X	X
Filigree Skimmer	*Pseudoleon superbus*					X	X
Variegated Meadowhawk*	*Sympetrum corruptum*	X	X	X	X	X	X
Saffron-winged Mhawk*	*S. costiferum*	X	X	X	X		X
Black Meadowhawk*	*S. danae*	X	X	X	X	X	X
Cardinal Meadowhawk*	*S. illotum*	X	X			X	X
Cherry-faced Meadowhawk	*S. internum*	X	X	X	X		X
Red-veined Meadowhawk	*S. madidum*	X	X	?	X		
White-faced Meadowhawk	*S. obtrusum*	X	X	X	X		X

COMMON NAME	SCIENTIFIC NAME	CA	NV	UT	CO	AZ	NM
DRAGONFLIES	**ANISOPTERA**						
Western Meadowhawk*	*S. occidentale*	X	X	X	X	X	X
Striped Meadowhawk*	*S. pallipes*	X	X	X	X	X	X
Ruby Meadowhawk	*S. rubicundulum*				X		
Spot-winged Meadowhawk	*S. signiferum*					X	
Yellow-legged Mhawk.	*S. vicinum*	X			X	X	X
Striped Saddlebags	*Tramea calverti*					X	
Black Saddlebags*	*T. lacerata*	X	X	X	X	X	X
Red Saddlebags*	*T. onusta*	X	X	X	X	X	X
EMERALDS	**CORDULIIDAE**						
American Emerald*	*Cordulia shurtleffii*	X	X	X	X		
Beaverpond Baskettail*	*Epitheca canis*	X					
Common Baskettail	*E. cynosura*				X		
Dot-winged Baskettail	*E. petechialis*				X		X
Spiny Baskettail*	*E. spinigera*	X					
Orange Shadowdragon	*Neurocordulia xanthosoma*				X		?
Ringed Emerald*	*Somatochlora albincinta*	X					
Plains Emerald	*S. ensigera*				X		
Hudsonian Emerald	*S. hudsonica*				X		
Ocellated Emerald	*S. minor*				X		
Mountain Emerald*	*S. semicircularis*	X	X	X	X		X
DARNERS	**AESHNIDAE**						
Canada Darner	*Aeshna canadensis*	X					
Lance-tipped Darner	*A. constricta*		?	X	X		X
Lake Darner	*A. eremita*			X	X		
Variable Darner	*A. interrupta*	X	X	X	X	X	X
Sedge Darner	*A. juncea*			X	X		X
Paddle-tailed Darner*	*A. palmata*	X	X	X	X	X	X
Persephone's Darner	*A. persephone*				X	X	X
Zigzag Darner	*A. stichensis*				X		
Shadow Darner*	*A. umbrosa*	X	X	X	X		X

154

COMMON NAME	SCIENTIFIC NAME	STATE					
		CA	NV	UT	CO	AZ	NM
DRAGONFLIES	ANISOPTERA						
Walker's Darner*	A. walkeri	X	X				
Common Green Darner*	Anax junius	X	X	X	X	X	X
Giant Darner*	A. walsinghami	X	X	X		X	X
Riffle Darner	Oplonaeschna armata	X		X		X	X
Malachite Darner	Remartinia luteipennis					X	
California Darner*	Rhionaeschna californica	X	X	X	X		
Turquoise Darner	R. psilus					X	
Arroyo Darner	R. dugesi					X	X
Blue-eyed Darner*	R. multicolor	X	X	X	X	X	X
CLUBTAIL	GOMPHIDAE						
Flag-tailed Spinyleg	Dromogomphus spoliatus						X
White-belted Ringtail*	Erpetogomphus compositus	X	X	X		X	X
Yellow-legged Ringtail	E. crotalinus					X	X
Eastern Ringtail	E. designatus		X		X	X	X
Dashed Ringtail	E. heterodon						X
Serpent Ringtail	E. lampropeltis	X				X	X
Plains Clubtail	Gomphus externus			X			X
Pronghorn Clubtail	G. graslinellus				X		
Pacific Clubtail*	G. kurilis	X					
Sulphur-tipped Clubtail	G. militaris				X		X
Grappletail*	Octogomphus specularis	X	X				
Arizona Snaketail	Ophiogomphus arizonicus					X	X
Bison Snaketail*	O. bison	X	X	X			
Great Basin Snaketail*	O. morrisoni	X	X				
Sinuous Snaketail*	O. occidentis	X	X	X	?		
Pale Snaketail*	O. severus	X	X	X	X		X
Five-striped Leaftail	Phyllogomphoides albrighti						X
Four-striped Leaftail	P. stigmatus						X
Gray Sanddragon*	Progomphus borealis	X	X	X		X	X
Common Sanddragon	P. obscurus				X		X
Brimstone Clubtail	Stylurus intricatus	X	X	X		X	X

COMMON NAME	SCIENTIFIC NAME	STATE					
DRAGONFLIES	ANISOPTERA	CA	NV	UT	CO	AZ	NM
Olive Clubtail	*S. olivaceus*	X	X	X			
Russet-tipped Clubtail	*S. plagiatus*	X	X			X	X
PETALTAILS	PETALURIDAE	CA	NV	UT	CO	AZ	NM
Black Petaltail*	*Tanypteryx hageni*	X	X				
SPIKETAILS	CORDULEGASTERIDAE	CA	NV	UT	CO	AZ	NM
Apache Spiketail	*Cordulegaster diadema*			X		X	X
Pacific Spiketail*	*C. dorsalis*	X	X	X	X		X
CRUISERS	MACROMIIDAE	CA	NV	UT	CO	AZ	NM
Bronzed River Cruiser	*Macromia annulata*						X
Western River Cruiser*	*M. magnifica*	X	X	X		X	
COMMON NAME	SCIENTIFIC NAME	STATE					
DAMSELFLIES	ZYGOPTERA	CA	NV	UT	CO	AZ	NM
BROAD-WINGED	CALOPTERYGIDAE						
River Jewelwing*	*Calopteryx aequabilis*	X	X	X	X		
Ebony Jewelwing	*C. maculata*				X		
American Rubyspot*	*Hetaerina americana*	X	X	X	X	X	X
Smokey Rubyspot	*H. titia*						X
Canyon Rubyspot	*H. vulnerata*			X		X	X
SPREADWINGS	LESTIDAE	CA	NV	UT	CO	AZ	NM
California Spreadwing*	*Archilestes californicus*	X	X			X	
Great Spreadwing*	*A. grandis*	X		X	X	X	X
Plateau Spreadwing	*Lestes alacer*					X	X
Spotted Spreadwing*	*L. congener*	X	X	X	X	X	X
Common Spreadwing*	*L. disjunctus*	X	X	X	X	X	X
Emerald Spreadwing*	*L. dryas*	X	X	X	X	X	X
Sweetflag Spreadwing	*L. forcipatus*				X		
Slender Spreadwing	*L. rectangularis*				X		
Black Spreadwing*	*L. stultus*	X					
Lyre-tipped Spreadwing*	*L. unguiculatus*	X	X	X	X		

COMMON NAME	SCIENTIFIC NAME	STATE					
		CA	NV	UT	CO	AZ	NM
DAMSELFLIES	ZYGOPTERA						
SHADOWDAMSELS	PLATYSTICTIDAE						
Desert Shadow Damsel	Palaemnema domina					X	
POND DAMSELS	COENAGRIONIDAE	CA	NV	UT	CO	AZ	NM
Western Red Damsel*	Amphiagrion abbreviatum	X	X	X	X	X	X
Black and White Damsel	Apanisagrion lais					X	
California Dancer*	Argia agrioides	X	X			X	
Paiute Dancer	A. alberta	X	X	X	X	X	X
Blue-fronted Dancer	A. apicalis				X	X	X
Emma's Dancer*	A. emma	X	X	X	X		
Spine-tipped Dancer	A. extranea					X	
Variable Dancer	A. fumipennis				X	X	X
Lavender Dancer	A. hinei	X	X			X	X
Kiowa Dancer	A. immunda	X	X			X	X
Leonora's Dancer	A. leonorae						X
Sierra Madre Dancer	A. lacrimans					X	
Sooty Dancer*	A. lugens	X	?	X	X	X	X
Powdered Dancer	A. moesta	X	X	X	X	X	X
Apache Dancer	A. munda			X		X	X
Aztec Dancer*	A. nahuana	X	X	X	X	X	X
Fiery-eyed Dancer	A. oenea					X	
Amethyst Dancer	A. pallens					X	X
Pima Dancer	A. pima					X	
Springwater Dancer	A. plana				X	X	X
Sabino Dancer	A. sabino					X	
Blue-ringed Dancer*	A. sedula	X	X	X	X	X	X
Tarascan Dancer	A. tarascana					X	
Tezpi Dancer	A. tezpi					X	X
Tonto Dancer	A. tonto					X	X
Dusky Dancer	A. translata					X	X
Vivid Dancer*	A. vivida	X	X	X	X	X	X

COMMON NAME	SCIENTIFIC NAME	STATE					
DAMSELFLIES	ZYGOPTERA	CA	NV	UT	CO	AZ	NM
Taiga Bluet	*Coenagrion resolutum*	X		X	X	X	
River Bluet	*Enallagma anna*	X	X	X	X		X
Rainbow Bluet	*E. antennatum*				X		
Double-striped Bluet	*E. basidens*	X			X	X	X
Boreal Bluet*	*E. boreale*	X	X	X	X	X	X
Tule Bluet*	*E. carunculatum*	X	X	X	X	X	X
Familiar Bluet*	*E. civile*	X	X	X	X	X	X
Alkali Bluet*	*E. clausum*	X	X	X	X		X
Northern Bluet*	*E. cyathigerum*	X	X	X	X	X	X
Marsh Bluet	*E. ebrium*			X			
Hagen's Bluet	*E. hageni*				X		
Arroyo Bluet*	*E. praevarum*	X	X	X	X	X	X
Claw-tipped Bluet	*E. semicirculare*					X	X
Vesper Bluet	*E. vesperum*				X		
Painted Damsel	*Hesperagrion heterodoxum*				X	X	X
Desert Forktail	*Ischnura barberi*	X	X	X		X	X
Pacific Forktail*	*I. cervula*	X	X	X	X	X	X
Plains Forktail	*I. damula*				X	X	X
Mexican Forktail	*I. demorsa*				X	X	X
Black-fronted Forktail*	*I. denticollis*	X	X	X	X	X	X
Swift Forktail	*I. erratica*	X					
San Francisco Forktail*	*I. gemina*	X					
Citrine Forktail	*I. hastata*	X	X		X	X	X
Western Forktail*	*I. perparva*	X	X	X	X	X	X
Rambur's Forktail	*I. ramburii*	X	X			X	X
Eastern Forktail	*I. verticalis*				X		X
Sedge Sprite	*Nehalennia irene*	X					
Desert Firetail*	*Telebasis salva*	X	X	X		X	X
Exclamation Damsel*	*Zoniagrion exclamationis*	X					

FAQ (Frequently Asked Questions)

How long do they live? As flying adults, dragonflies live only a few weeks, but if you include their underwater stage as nymph/larva, their life-span is one summer to three years.

What do they eat? Adult flying dragonflies eat other smaller flying insects, esp. mosquitoes and gnats. Larva eat other underwater life forms such as mosquito larvae. Larger nymphs can and will eat pollywogs and small fish.

Where do they go in the winter? Adult dragonflies die of old age as winter approaches, but larva from spring, summer and fall laid eggs are still maturing underwater.

How many kinds are there? On Earth there are over 5,400 species of dragonflies and damselflies. In the USA and Canada there are 435 species altogether. New species are still being discovered, even here in the USA.

Do they bite or sting? Dragonflies do not have stingers and cannot sting! Since they have a mouth, they can bite, but they bite prey, not humans, unless handled roughly. Their bite would be like a hard pinch.

Can they darn your lips closed? Of course not! An old folk tale said that if you told lies a dragonfly would darn your lips closed. However, there are other bad consequences that befall those who tell lies!

Were they really here when dinosaurs were on Earth? Yes! Dragonflies have existed for over 200 million years! In fact, they were here before the dinosaurs, and are among the most ancient creatures still populating our planet Earth.

Websites and discussion groups:

DRAGONFLIES OF THE SOUTHWEST:
http://southwestdragonflies.net/

ARIZONA ODONATES:
http://www.azodes.com/main/default.asp

CALIFORNIA DRAGONFLIES:
http://www.sonic.net/dragonfly/

NEW MEXICO DRAGONFLY NOTEBOOK:
http://www.rt66.com/~kjherman/odonata/notebook.html

Western U.S. Odonata Range Maps
http://www.ups.edu/biology/museum/westernOD.html

CalOdes discussion group:
http://groups.yahoo.com/group/CalOdes/

SoWest Odes discussion group:
http://groups.yahoo.com/group/SoWestOdes/

To order
Common Dragonflies of the Southwest
and/or
Common Dragonflies of California, A Beginner's Pocket Guide

Write to
Azalea Creek Publishing
attn: Kathy Biggs

azalea@sonic.net
or
308 Bloomfield Rd.
Sebastopol, CA 95472
and/or

visit a nearby park, nature or book store